OPENING POEM：扉詩

Linked Haiku.：連句

Edo
恵道

pulling weeds
mosquitoes on my back
have a picnic

草取りや僕の背中で蚊のピクニック
kusa tori ya, boku no senaka de ka no, pikuniku

noriko
水崎野里子

the summer so hot
sparing the air conditioner
a round fan better

暑き夏エアコンけちって団扇かな
atsuki natsu eakon kechitte utiwa kana

＜発刊の辞＞

出帆の日来たる

パンドラ筐に

なにもかも詰め入れ

荒海に乗り出でん

いざ共に　錨を上げよ

水崎野里子

The day has come

To hoist sails!

Putting everything

Into Pandora casket

We are ready to start

Noriko

パンドラ
目次

Pandora
Contents

岡山晴彦（日本・熊本・神奈川）

Haruhiko Okayama (Japan / Kumamoto / Kanagawa)

石榴の実:　短歌五首

The Pomegranate Fruit & Other Tanka Poems

石榴の実われは血と言ひ彼の女はルビーとつぶやくその唇よ
The fruit of a pomegranate there
I am referring it as blood yet still
The woman sitting opposite to me
She murmurs it as ruby to herself
See you her lips are red and split!

枯れ果てし蝶の骸の軽きこと草蜘蛛の糸幽か揺れたり
Withered to the end and life is gone
The butterfly is dead and stark now
It is so light an' how it light I wonder
I see the threads a grass spider span
Have a faint swing into a bit of sway

捨てられし黒薔薇の造花怖れつつ靴の先にて道の端に寄す
I found it deserted on a stone pavement
An artificial flower it was in a black rose
I feel it weird and of unlucky I am afraid
Frightening and terrifying of it I get then
A tip of my shoe put it aside onto the edge

パリーンと夜の声あれは三日月の落ちる音ですよと母さんの声
I heard the sound as parin a cracking like
The voice of night it was from a darkness
A voice of mom is telling me high up some
That is a sound of the crescent moon high
Coming down falling on the earth echoing

青柿の青き茂みよ青青青青きものへのわが妬みかなし
The persimmons are green and young not ripe
The shrubs and clusters in the color of green!
They look green and green so much green oh!
Of all the things in color of green on the earth
That I am jealous and not can stop it is a pity!

(English Translator: Noriko Mizusaki)

近況

日頃親しい友人に翻訳家がいる。その外語大英語科の仲間内で、往年の松村みね子氏が話題に上り、遇々同氏翻訳掲載の『英国戯曲集』(昭和初期新潮社『世界文学全集』を私が所持しており、所望され回覧に供する。うち愛蘭(アイルランド)作家シングの「海へ騎りゆく者たち」は、青年の頃魅入られた作品(私の原点)である。岡本綺堂等の戯曲を収めた『明治大正文学全集』(昭和初期、春陽堂)、社会派詩劇の先駆者、近松門左衛門の『近松浄瑠璃傑作集』(昭28　春陽堂)も久し振りに手に取ってみる。

最近、早稲田大学の演劇博物館で、前進座の第一回「ベニスの商人」の記録映画(白黒)を鑑賞する。終戦後同館の前庭で最初に上演され、全国の学校へ巡演された。旧制熊本中学の時、元兵舎の仮校舎(空襲で焼失)で、河原崎長十郎丈、しづ江で劇が上演された懐かしい憶い出がある。(同館に拙著詩劇蔵)

時折、新歌舞伎座に祀る稲荷大明神に詣でるが、熊本から上京進学の年、昭和二六年に旧歌舞伎座が再開したのを思い出す。当時近くの月島に住み、貧乏学生なりに通う。梨園皆先代となったが、晩年の吉右衛門、まだ海老蔵の団十郎、歌右衛門、幸四郎、松緑丈など戦後の劇界を彩り華々しかった。

二〇年続く自主講座「沙翁会」が本年閉会、シェークスピア、希臘(ギリシャ)から西欧近代迄の戯曲は良き糧となる。木下順二師(中学の先輩)には紙上私淑する。

今、早稲田大学(母校)の「歌舞伎と文楽」の講座に通う。同じ場面を対比して、役者の演技の個性と浄瑠璃に人形を繰る太夫の技の力が見え興味深い。

京都太秦の日活等で、若き日の山田五十鈴(十六歳)や片岡千恵蔵丈(三十歳)と並んだ私の写真が、生後六か月の時と判明。これも縁か。(熊本出生の筈の私だが)

(「『衣』47号近況」より)

解説：岡山晴彦氏は劇作家・歌人・詩人。「Pegada19」(2019夏号)の氏の新作戯曲「今様お伽話　麦の穂」(セリフに七五調を含めた)を拝見し、本誌への再度の寄稿を今度は短歌のご寄稿としてお願いした。

なお、坪内逍遥で始まったシェークスピアの日本語翻訳は、現在では意味伝達を重視し、セリフの音韻リズムを除外・無視した口語訳がむしろ「現代語訳」として人気である。だが、ある一団の学者間ではむしろ七五調訳に戻る、あるいは、初めから全篇七五調を含めて訳しなおすべきではないか？そちらの方がより国際的であり「現代的」であるのではないか？との疑問も出ている。シュークスピアはセリフにブランクヴァースと言われる弱強五脚・無押韻の韻文形式を多く使用した。特にこの疑問は、シングやW.B.イェイツの戯曲を学んだアイルランド文学関係の研究者からの発言・提言・疑問であることが多い。なお、熊本にも一時住んだ木下順二の日本民話を使用した「詩劇」は、同じくアイルランド民話運動とシェークスピアの詩劇を手本としながら、あるいはまさに外国文学を基本の手本としたゆえに、七五調よりもむしろ方言使用に詩劇性と喜劇性を見た。シングの応用（「西の国の伊達男」など）である。だが、それは言い換えれば日本の能を手本としたW.B.イエイツの詩劇（狂言翻案にもブランクヴァース使用）の音韻性には及ばず、日本の「戦後期（第二芸術論）」に妥協の散文性ではないか？との私の印象がある。（水崎の勘違い？であればご指摘いただきたい）。

2019年10月1日、水崎野里子記。

藤田晴央（日本・弘前）

乳色の空から

奥深い乳色の空に
不意にあらわれるものがある
空の高みを羽ばたいている

鴨だろうか
雁だろうか
見きわめかねているうちに
鳥は　また
乳色の空に　隠れるように入っていった
もうひとつの世界から
あやまって出てきて
あやまちに気づいたように
もうひとつの世界に戻っていった

雪粒は
空の奥から
あらわれ　あらわれつづけ
わたしの体を過ぎて
地上に降り立ち続ける

鳥も
雪も
わたしの知らない
もうひとつの世界からあらわれる

あなたも
そのようにあらわれた
願わくば
鳥のようにではなく
雪のように

Haruo Fujita (Japan / Hirosaki)

From a Milky Colored Sky

In a milky colored sky so thick
Something appears unexpectedly
Fluttering now high in the sky

A wild duck?
A wild goose?
While I could not tell
The bird flew back
Deep to hide himself
Just like
He had come out
Of the other world
In mistake
Having realized it
He returned there

From the depth of the sky
Snow drops out falling
Keep appearing one after another
Passing by me
Falling up thick on the earth

The bird
The snow
Appeared
From the other world
Unknown to me

You came out
In the same way with them

わたしをつつんで
降り積もってほしい
あなたも　わたしも
この世にあらわれたのは
あやまちではないのだから

初出：「交野が原」86号（2019年4月）

Yet I wish
Not like the bird
Just like the snow
May you fall down thick
Shrouding me

Both you and me
Appeared on this earth
That is not a mistake

(Translator: Haruo Fujita & Noriko Mizusaki)
First publication in Japanese：
“Katanogahara” No.86 (April,2019)

蛇紋岩

流れてゆくものがある
水の底には蛇紋岩
青緑の光をはなちながら
蛇のようにすずやかに光っている

尾根筋からやってくる人がいる
わたしの知らない山肌をのぼり
わたしの知らない谷をふりかえりながら
やってきた人
ここにかがんで
一緒に湧き水をのみましょう
水の底には蛇紋岩

ひとりのための旋律と
もうひとりのための旋律がまじりあい
弦楽がからみあい
渓流がしぶきをあげている
蛇のようにすずやかに

わたしはあなたの知らない沢をのぼり
あなたの知らない空をあおぎながら
やってきた
この水は太古の味がする
この星が誕生してまもないころの
地層がくだけちったこの岩は
むきだしで
もろい
わたしたちのように

青緑の蛇紋岩は
水をしたたらせた蛇のように
うつくしいひとすじの道となり

Der Serpentin[i]

Da fließt etwas
Serpentin auf dem Grunde des Gebirgsbachs.
Während er blaugrünes Licht abgibt,
leuchtet er kühl wie eine Schlange.

Vom Grat kommt jemand herunter.
Sie ist auf einen Berg gestiegen, den ich nicht kenne,
sie hat auf ein Tal geschaut, das ich nicht kenne,
die Frau, die gekommen ist.
Lass uns hinunterbeugen und
gemeinsam das sprudelnde Quellwasser trinken.
Ein Serpentin auf dem Grunde des Gebirgsbachs.

Die Melodie für den einen und
die Melodie für einen anderen mischen sich,
Streichmusikklänge umschlingen einander,
der Gebirgsbach sprudelt wild,
kühl wie eine Schlange.

Ich steige einen Bach zwischen den Bergen hinauf, den du nicht kennst,
hinaufschauend zu einem Himmel, den du nicht kennst,
bin ich gekommen.
Dieses Wasser schmeckt nach uralten Zeiten.
Aus der Zeit unmittelbar nach Entstehen des Planeten
stammt dieser Stein aus der aufgebrochenen Erdschicht.

Er ist nackt
und zerbrechlich
wie wir.

Der blaugrüne Serpentin ist
wie eine vor Wasser triefende Schlange,

山頂へとつづいている
ここからは
ひとすじの道

初出：「歴程」597号（2016年）

er ist wie ein schöner Weg ohne Abzweigungen.
Er geht bis zum Gipfel
von hier aus
der gerade Weg.

Erstveröffentlichung: *Rekitei*[ii] Nr. 597 (2016).
Übersetzung: Haruo Fujita / Monika Unkel

---

[i] Serpentin oder fachsprachlich eigentlich Serpentinit ist ein metamorphes Gestein. Früher wurde es auch als Schlangensteine bezeichnet. Das japanische Wort für Serpentin *jamongan* 蛇紋岩 kommt in Gedichten von Miyazawa Kenji vor und steht dort für einen blaugrünen schönen Stein.

[ii] *Rekitei* ist eine Zeitschrift für moderne japanische Dichtung.

林宏匡（日本・東京・松江）
Hiromasa Hayashi (Japan / Tokyo / Matsue)

『ホムルスクの夕日』より
From *The Setting Sun in Holmsk**

郷愁
Nostalgia

なぎさ辺に昆布を拾へる弟も爺と呼ばるる齢なりしか
On the beach my brother picking up konbu: the seaweed
He has come to the age called granpa: many years passed

拾ひ來し昆布に憶ひをめぐらせて羽母舞原野に囲むバーベキュー
Thinking of the konbu he picked up to come back to all
On the Khabomai wilderness we sat around a barbecue

※ホルムスクはサハリン州の都市。現在ロシア連邦の実効支配が及ぶ。樺太南部に位置し、日本名は真岡。

浜梨は変らぬ色に咲けれども六十二年前の日々は還らず
Sweetbriers blooming out in the same color with the olden
Though my old days; sixty two years ago shall not return

弟の差し出す鮭の燻製を何気なく取り噛みしむる旅
My brother gave me a piece of the salmon smoked
I took to chew it as if indifferent: it in my journey

離岸せむ船のエンヂン昂（たかぶ）れば愁（おも）ひふるはすサハリンの旅
For sailing out: the engine of the ship had rose up when
Nostalgia shaken go rising up: in my journey to Sakhalin

(Translator: Noriko Mizusaki)

働淳（日本・北九州）
Jun Hataraki (Japan / Northern Kyushu)

崎津へ
To Sakitsu

色とりどりに輝くステンドグラス
光る風、薫る波、流れる雲
ゴシック様式の崎津
ロマネスク様式の大江
かつて『五足の靴』で訪れた北原白秋が
その神父や潜伏キリシタンに想いを馳せて
『邪宗門』を書いた祈りの地
島原、長崎、平戸、五島と海で繋がり
世界遺産となって人を惹きつけている

Stained glasses in the various colors vivid and bright
Shining breezes and fragrant waves: clouds go flow
Sakitsu Church in the Gothic architecture
Oe church in the Romanesque style
The area once a Japanese poet Hakushu Kitahara visited for travelling essays with other four poets of his friends
They were published finally in a book: *The Five Pairs of Shoes*
Then he published his poetry book *Jashumon*: *The Prohibited Faith*
He remembered the priests and the hidden Christians for prayers
The area can be linked with Shimabara: Nagasak: Hirato: and Goto in the sea route
Appointed as the world heritage it has been attracting tourists

ここで絵踏みが行われていたんです
神社の氏子となっても祈っていたんです
アワビやタイラギの貝殻の模様をマリアに見立て
柱を刳り貫いた穴にメダイを隠して
命懸けで守り、祈るものがあった

"Here they were forced to take the loyalty tests:
Stepping the Christ or Mary image engraved on a plank or a plate
They were secretly praying to them even when they were forced to be the members of Shintoism shrines"
Some of them imagined Mary in the patterns of the seashells:
the abalones or taigai shellfish
Some of them hid a medieval fish in a hole pierced through a wooden pole
They kept it protecting on the risk of their lives and offered secret prayers

通りにしめ縄が並ぶ木造家屋の漁師町
その家々の隙間のトウヤ（路地）を抜けると海に漁船が並んでいる
家のカケからすぐ船に乗って、海から世界にも繋がっている
そんな船を眺めていると海を渡り、時を越え
何処までもどこまでも想いは広がっていく

It is a fishers' village with their wooden houses
On the street line up thick twisted straw ropes in Shintoism
Striding through the lanes between houses I saw fishing boats on the sea
From kind of verandahs of their houses they can ride boats: the sea links to the world
Seeing them I feel like sailing across the sea beyond time
My imaginations go expand endless

いま私は何を信じ、祈りを捧げているのか
気付かぬうちに絵踏みをして
日々選んでいるこの生活の
行き着く果てはどこに

What do I believe now to offer prayers?
I am spending my days stepping on the holy figures
Without any consciousness: in my choice?
I wonder where my life would go adrift at the end

教会が海に浮かび
海のマリア像が

航海の無事を見守っている

The church goes float up in the sea
The Mary statue stands high up on the seaside hill
Watching our sails for safety

(Translator: Noriko Mizusaki)

藤谷恵一郎（日本・大阪）

一粒の砂

一粒の砂があるということは
宇宙があるということ

一粒の砂があるということは
億年の時の広がりがあるということ

一粒の砂があるということは
豊かな水があるということ

君がいるということは
未来があるということ

Keiichiro Fujitani (Japan / Osaka)

A Grain of Sand

A grain of sand is here:
The existence of the universe I have

A grain of sand is here:
A time expanse for millions years I have

A grain of sand is here:
Abundant water I have

You are here:
The future I have in my hand

(Translated by Yumiko Yamamoto & Noriko Mizusaki)

吉田健一（日本・大阪）

白っぽい風景の中で

こんなかんかん照りの夏の真昼に
あなたは黒いこうもり傘を差して
照り返すアスファルトの長い坂道を下りてゆきます

青ざめた顔をして通り過ぎようとする私に
あなたはためらいも警戒もせず笑いかけてくれます

そしてあなたは以前からの友人のように
私の頭にこうもり傘を差しかけてくれて
たわいもない話を　話し続けてくれます

朽ちかけた寺の土塀越しに
十メートルもある墓石が二つ
天に向かってそそり立っています

志納所であなたと私は
入山料を百五十円ずつ渡すのですが
寺務員は坐ったまま氷のように動きません

「今日は宝物殿は休みなのでしょう」
そう言い合ってあなたと私は
真夏の白っぽい墓地の中をデートします

「あなたが好きです」唐突に
私がそう言うと　あなたは
私の知らない方言で答えるのですが

それは「ほんとうですか」とも「うそでしょう」とも
とれるようなニュアンスです

Ken-ichi Yoshida (Japan / Osaka)

In the Landscape Dazzling White

At the high noon in the summer so heated and hot
You are walking down holding up a black umbrella
On the long asphalt slope: it bounces heat back

Feeling sick with the heat I am about to pass you
When you smile to me with no hesitation or no cares

Then holding up the umbrella over me
As if you have been an old friend of mine
You keep talking to me on the things not serious

Over the clay wall of the old temple I see
The two gravestones taller than ten meters
Pop out sticking high up in the sky

At the entrance of the yard you and I have to pay
The admission fee each for one hundred fifty yen
But the clerk stays sitting and does not move like ice

"Today the treasure hall is closed"
Chatting we are each other and start enjoying a date
We walk in the heated graveyard in the mid-summer

"I love you" abruptly say I to you when
You answer me in a dialect strange to me

In the nuance I can take for either of them:
"Is it true?" or "it is a lie!"

White smokes of the incense hit my nose acute

白い線香の煙　ツーンと鼻を突きます

私は喜びもなく悲しみもなく
あなたの顔の
白っぽい風景を見つめています

「生きているのはあなたと私だけね」

そう言ってから　あなたは　私の顔の上に
差しかけていた黒いこうもり傘を
いつまでもいつまでも
クルクルクルクル　回し続けているのです

I have nothing but to watch the landscape white
Behind your face: at the backward of you

“Just you and me are alive here you know”

Saying so you start turning the umbrella
You were just now holding up over me
Around and around: you keep turning it
As if it with no ends: it be forever

(Translator: Noriko Mizusaki)

長津功三良（日本・岩国）

『わが基地物語・序章』より

わたしは　生まれも　育ちも　ひろしまだが
ピカドンには　遭わなかった
原爆投下の　直前直後に　広島に居たが
祖母の家に疎開していて　被爆せず
あれから　大きな荷物を背負って　生きながらえている
キリストではないから
十字架を　背負っているとは　言わないが
自分なりに　生涯の　引け目を背負っている
それは　昏く　昏く　重い

長い間　「ひろしま」のことを　自分なりに　書き続けてきたが
無差別殺戮（ジェノサイド）の　惨状を知るだけに
聞き取り　記録し　次の世代へ
語り継ぐべき　責務を　背負っているひとり
周りから　次第に　被爆者たちが　消えている
かれら　かのじょら
もう　薄れかけた　影たちの仲間に　なってきている

見たこと　聞いたこと　考えたこと
マンネリでも良い
繰り返し記録していこう
もう　わたしにも　残りの時間が　僅少（すくな）くなっている
そのためにも　繰り返し　語らねばならないのだ

あの　灼けて　燃えた　夏の日の　記憶のために
わが　生の　ある限り……

Kozaburo Nagatsu (Japan / Iwakuni)

From *My Story on the Base*

The Opening Poem

I was born and brought up in Hiroshima though
Fortunately I was not attacked by the Pikadon
Just before and after the Atomic bombing I stayed in Hiroshima
I relocated to my grandmother's house where I did not have
the radiation exposure but.
Since then I manage to survive carrying a big load on the back
I was not a Christ
So I would not say I carry the cross on the back
Yet I carry myself a kind of the handicap lifelong on the back
It is gloomy: so gloomy and heavy

For a long time on Hiroshima I have been writing as hard as I could
Because I know real miseries of the Genocide
I shall be the one of them who have to listen to and record them
To talk down to the next generation: I carry the responsibility on the back
Gradually A-bomb survivors disappeared one by one from around me
They: men and women are making friends with the shadows fading away

What I saw: What I heard: What I thought:
I shall record them noting down repeatedly
I do not mind if you call me in the mannerism
Now my lifetime left is becoming shorter and shorter
For that reason I have to talk on them in the repetitions

For the memory of that summer day scorched and burned
In so long as I am alive: till at the end of my life

(Translator: Noriko Mizusaki)

尾崎まこと（日本・大阪）

立っているのは？

立っているのは
誰ですか
骨ですか
血ですか
昨日の僕ですか

立っているのは
誰ですか
陽炎ですか
幽霊ですか
明日の思い出ですか

座っているのは
誰ですか
言葉ですか
全くでたらめですか
絶望ですか

歩き始めたのは
誰ですか
愛ですか
愛ですよ
愛ですよ

Makoto Ozaki (Japan / Osaka)

Who Is Standing?

Who is standing?
Who is it?
A bone?
Blood?
Or the me of the day gone by?

Who is standing?
Who is it?
A mirage?
A ghost?
Or a memory from tomorrow?

Who is sitting?
Who is it?
Words?
Complete nonsense?
Or despair?

Who started marching?
Who is it?
Is it love?
Yes, it is.
Love it is.

(Translator: Yumiko Yamamoto)

月の砂漠

On the Desert of the Moon

ラクダに揺られて今宵も砂漠をゆく。
夢から覚めて月を観たと言ってはならない。
身体を失くした俺がことばのラクダに乗せられ
月という明るいことばを見上げたのだ！

I also go travel tonight on the desert riding on a camel: rocked to and fro
You must not tell me in waking up from a dream I looked up at the moon in the sky
My spirit having lost the body gave me a lift on the word of camel: to look up at the bright word of the moon

(Translator: Noriko Mizusaki)

モーツアルト広場にて　In the Mozart Square
ザルツブルグ 2019 年 8 月末　In Saltzburg: August,2019.
水崎野里子撮影　photo by Noriko Mizusaki

月の砂漠

ラクダに揺られて今夜も砂漠をゆく。
夢から覚めて月を観たと言ってはならない。
身体を失くした俺がことばのラクダに乗せられ月という明るいことばを見上げたのだ。

尾崎まこと
Ozaki Makoto

左子真由美（日本・長岡京）

輪郭

りんごをなぞるように
きみのりんかくをなぞる
ふしぎだ
せかいと
きみとに
さかいめがあるなんて

Mayumi Sako (Japan / Nagaokakyo)

On Your Figure

Like tracing an apple
I trace your figure
It is strange
You have a borderline
Between you
And the world

(Translator: Noriko Mizusaki)

野咲（ノエミ）――四歳の孫娘に

のえちゃんは　はんたいがすき
いただきます　っていうと
ごちそうさま　っていう
のえちゃんは　いたずらがすき
トウモロコシ　っていえる？　ってきくと
トウロモコシ　とこたえてわらう

まるくやわらかい　のえちゃん
パンみたいに　ふわふわ
はるかぜとくさの　においがする
つかまえよう　とすると
のうさぎみたいに　スルリ
てを　すりぬける

のえちゃんは　よんさい
せなかには　まだはねがある
せかいにたったひとりの　のえちゃん
これから　だいぼうけんのたびにでる
はねにひっかけた　ちいさなリュックに
たからものを　いっぱいつめて

Noemi——To My Four-year-old Granddaughter

Noe-chan likes to be contrary.
If I were to say, “Bon appétit!”
She says, “I’m full” even before she starts.
Noe-chan likes teasing me.
If I ask, “Can you say ‘To-Mo-Ro-Ko-Shi’?”*
She smiles back and says, “To-Ro-Mo-Ko-Shi.”

Plump Noe-chan,
As soft as bread,
Smells of spring breeze and grass.
If I try to grab her,
She slips through my hands
Like a rabbit.

Noe-chan is just four,
With the wings on her back still.
The only one in the world,
She is about to start her adventure
With her treasures filling up,
The small backpack on her wings.

*Note=Tomorokoshi means corn in Japanese.

(Translator: Yumiko Yamamoto)

扉よ

わたしは今日
何度扉を開けただろう
そして昨日は
そして明日は
日夜
掠り傷のついたノブをまわして
少しばかり新しい風を入れて

思えば
生きるとは
扉を開けることであった

何千回
何万回
いいえ何百万回
ああ　数えきれないほど

さようなら　と
後ろ手で閉じた扉もあった
けれど　いつも幸せをもとめて
扉を開きつづけた

いつしか扉の後ろには
思い出の砂浜が広がり
残ったのは何とたどたどしい足跡

それでも　なお
こんにちは　と
わたしは明日の扉を開けるだろう
扉の向こうにひろがる
美しい夏の海が見たくて

To My Door

Today how many times
Did I open the door?
So did I yesterday?
So shall I tomorrow?
Day and night
Turning the knob with scratches
I put in a bit of fresh breeze
I think
To live has been
To open the door

Thousands times
Tens of thousands of times
No! Some millions times
So many times I cannot count

Good bye! Saying so
I once closed it behind my back
But always seeking for happiness
I opened it again and again

Sometime before I knew
The sandy beach in my nostalgia spreads
Before me
There! Left my footprints tottering

Even though still
Hello! Saying so
I shall open the door of tomorrow
Wishing to see the beautiful sea in the summer
Spreading beyond

(Translator: Noriko Mizusaki)

渡邊那智子（日本・東京）

短詩詩連

フリージヤ

凍れる
春の指

渚

いつの日も
太陽は歩んできて
過ぎることのない
思いを語る

黒揚羽

失楽の園を
逃れて

窓寄りの猫

いつしか灰となり
サフランの雨を降らせた

空蝉

彷徨う
秋が
見つけた

（初出「現代詩図鑑」2013年冬、2011年晩秋）

Nachiko Watanabe (Japan / Tokyo)

Short Poems

Freesia

Frozen finger
Of spring

Strand

Any day
The sun walks to me
And talks about love
That never passes away

Black Swallowtail

Fled
From Paradise Lost

Cat by Window

Reduced to ashes unnoticed
Let a saffron-rain fall

Cast-off Skin of Cicada

Found
By autumn
Wandering

(Translated by the author)

虹の涙
故秋元敏子氏に捧ぐ

ルノアールの描く「テラスにて」の貴婦人か。英国演劇の名花シドンズ夫人か。早春の庭に立つ伯母。片手で幼子の手を握り片腕に乳呑み子を抱えて二階の私を見上げている。「移るから駄目よ！」と制止する母を振り切り階段を駆け上がって来た。猩紅熱で一室に隔離されている瘡蓋だらけの私をぎゅっと抱きしめ「これで遊んで」と手渡してくれたふわふわの毛糸玉。ピンク、コバルト、ラヴェンダー、それから何色があったのか。戦時下の物不足の中、伯母が考え出した夢を紡ぐ贈り物。毛糸に混じる金糸銀糸が午後の陽光(ひざし)に煌めいていた。外地で育った伯母は戦時中ももんぺは佩かず黒の徳利セーターに黒ズボン、真紅の口紅だけが鮮やかだ。空襲の合間、自転車をとばして農家へ向かう。少女時代の振り袖を帯を芋に玉蜀黍に取り換えるのだ。伯母の夫は出征中。「こうするとおいしく見えますの」麩(ふすま)入りの大麦パンも子供の喜ぶ動物の形に焼く。大根を煮詰めて水飴を作り子供に与えるルールは「高射砲が鳴ったら一匙よ」古い毛布を子供のコートに仕立て上げ、フードには兎の耳を付けた。

前兆だったのだろうか。東京大空襲。全焼した家の焼け跡に熱く長く燻っていたピアノの弦。そのピアノで伯母はよく「銀波」を弾いていた。又或る夏の日、伯母に連れられ我が家を訪れた伯母のおしゃまな長女、三面鏡を見付けるなり走り寄り「チャムイカラチメマチョ」と小さな両手で鏡を閉じてしまった。にこにこと見守っていた伯母。終戦の翌年の二月、伯母の戦死した兄の遺骨が帰還した。その葬儀で大雨に当った伯母は高熱を出し有丈の蒲団で押えても震えが止まらなかった。慢性の栄養失調が災いしたのだろう。日に日に病は進み重い肺炎と診断された。もうペニシリンを打つ他はない。当時知られ始めた奇跡の薬を求めて伯母の夫は奔走した。幸いその薬を入手出来る医者が見つかり急ぎ往診を頼んだのだったが、その一本の注射で伯母はショック死した。苦難の時代を健気に生き自らの悲運を悟るいとまもなく逝った伯母よ。砂枕に首を固定された斜頸の我が子を病院に置いて帰るにしのびず、引き返しては窓越しに見詰め涙を流していた伯母よ。降りしきる雪の中我が家に引き取られた幼い姉妹。母が進駐軍から放出された取って置きのランチョンミートを皿に盛ると、「しゃけ」

Tears of Rainbow
Dedicated to the late Mrs. Toshiko Akimoto (1918 – 1946)

Was she the lady "On the Terras" drawn by Renoir or Madame Siddons, the past star actress of the British theatrical world?

She was my aunt standing in the garden in early spring. Clasping an infant by the hand, with a baby in her arm, she was looking up at me. I was isolated then in my upstairs room with scarlet fever. Paying no heed to my mother's warning "Don't draw near! You'll catch the desease!", she rushed up to me and held me tight covered as I was with scabs all over. "Try playing with these." she said and handed me some fluffy balls of knitting yarn, pink, cobalt blue, lavender and some other pastel shades I cannot call up. In time of war short of commodities she thought out such a present little girls could spin a dream with. Golden and silver threads woven into the balls were sparkling in the afternoon sunlight.

Brought up abroad, she was an excellent dresser. I didn't see her put on work pants gathered at the ankles which women were supposed to wear in wartime. She used to wear black turtleneck sweater and black slacks, her crimson lipstick shining. In the intervals of air raids she hastened to farmhouses by bicycle to exchange her kimonos and sashes she wore in her girlhood for some potatoes and Indian corns. Her husband was at the front. She baked bread from inferior oat mixed with bran in the shape of animals children liked, saying "It looks tasty in this way." She boiled down radish to make starch syrup and laid down a rule for her daughters: Every time a high-angle gun goes bang, you can take a spoonful of starch syrup. She sewed her daughters' overcoats from old blankets and put a rabbit's ear-shaped decorations on their hoods.

Was it a portent that the strings of her piano on which she would play "The Silver Wave" sputtered long and hot in the ruins of a fire when her house was burnt down by the Tokyo major air raid? Was it an omen, too, that one summer morning when she called at my house, her precocious daughter, on finding a dresser with three mirrors, ran to it and shut it with her small hands, saying "Let's shut it. I feel cold." My aunt watched her beamingly.

In February in the year succeeding the war's end the skeletal

と姉が声を上げた。妹は煮しめの椎茸に怯え声を出さずに泣いていた。

（初出「詩と思想」2017年8月号）

remains of her brother killed in battle returned home. In attending his funeral she was drenched in a heavy rain and caught a high fever. Tremor would not stop even after she put on as many futons as there were. Chronic malnutrition must have accelerated the progress of her illness. Day by day her condition became worse and finally it was diagnosed as serious pneumonia. Now there would be no other way than an injection of penicillin. Her husband ran about looking for the miraculous medicine that had just become known to the world. Fortunately he found a doctor who could get it and asked him to make a house call. The doctor came and gave her a penicillin injection. In an instant she died of shock from penicillin.

Auntie who lived unflinchingly through the hard times and left this world without even having time to know your own evil fate! Auntie who would run back to the window of the hospital and keep gazing at your new born baby with tears running down your cheeks! You could not bear to leave her there with her wryneck fixed between the sand pillows.

In a heavy snowstorm her little daughters were taken over to my house. My mother served them luncheon meat passed out by the Occupation Forces and kept in reserve for some special event of my family. At the sight of it the elder sister exclaimed, “Salmon!” The younger sobbed silently scared of shiitakes boiled down in soy sauce.

(Translated by the author)

Nancy Arbuthnot (Washington D.C. / USA)

Unicorn
From *Wild Washington*

Royal horse
with single horn
(symbol of purity in ancient tapestries),
the unicorn stares deep
into woods,
wishing to leap far
from this city lane
it names and guards.

Unicorn

Royal horse
with single horn
(symbol of purity
in ancient tapestries),
the unicorn stares deep
into woods,
wishing to leap far
from this city lane
it names and guards.

61

ナンシー・アーブスノット(米国・ワシントンD.C.)

ユニコーン (一角獣)
『野生のワシントン』より

王の馬
一角獣
(古代のタペストリーでは純粋さの象徴)
ユニコーンはじっと
森の奥を見つめている
この街の路地から
遠く跳んで行きたい
彼の名が付き　護る小径

(和訳：水崎野里子)
(Japanese Translation Noriko Mizusaki)
(イラスト：キャシー・エイブラムソン)
(Illustration: Cathy Abramson)

郡山直（日本・奄美大島・神奈川）

幼児期に覚えた島言葉の威力

ある日午後米国の町を歩いていたら
　　コリー犬が僕に突進してきた
東洋系の我が体型に気付いたか
　　己の匂いに気付いたのかな
咄嗟に我島での少年期思いだし
　　それに従って事態に対応
小学校からの帰り道犬に追われたら
　　体かがめて石拾う真似した
すると犬石投げられるのを怖がって
　　追うのをやめて引き返したのだ
米国の大学町でも背をかがめ
　　石を拾って投げる真似した
米国の町の通りには石ころは
　　無かったけれどコリー犬立ち止まった
そして我島の言葉で怒鳴っていた
　　「ダーリムン！ウチクッサリンド！」と
あの時は英語も日本語も口に出ず
　　喜界島言葉が無意識に出た
その言葉翻訳すると「この野郎！
　　ぶっ殺すぞ」という意味になる
するとその大きなコリー犬立ち止まり
　　方向変えて立ち去って行った
この体験幼児期に覚えた島言葉は
　　血の中にずっと流れている証明

Naoshi Koriyama
(Japan / Amamiooshima / Kanagawa)

Power of the Island Language Learned in my Childhood

One afternoon, when I was walking along the street
of a college town in America,
a large collie came dashing toward me.
Did the dog notice my Oriental body shape ?
Or did it catch a smell of mine?
Quickly, I thought of my childhood action
on the island, with which I dealt with the situation.
When we were chased by a dog on our way
from primary school, we would crouch,
pretending to pick up a stone.
Then, the dog, afraid of being hit with a stone,
would stop chasing us and turned back.
Also in the college town of America,
I crouched, pretending to pick up a stone.
Although there were no stones in the street
of the American town, the collie stopped.
Then, I found myself shouting angry word
in my island language, "Daarimun! Uchikussarindo!"
At that moment,
neither English nor Japanese came out of my lips,
but my Kikaijima language came out unconsciously.
If I translate the island words into other languages,
they would mean, "Hey, you! I'll hit you and kill you!"
Then the big collie stopped, turned around and walked away.
This experience in the American college town proves
the island language that I had learned in my childhood
was always flowing in my blood stream.

植木信子（日本・新潟）

移ろいゆく海

どこから始まってどこへゆくのだろう
居たというひとりの生は忘れ去られ　埋められてゆく
切れ切れの思い出が前後左右なく現れる
過ぎ去ったことは懐かしく
たとえるなら風
深い深い空を切り裂いて　緑の木の間　草むらの窪みから
風は起き小枝にぶつかり　花や草を揺らし吹いて来る
掴めない面影がふくながしのように流れ
一瞬　声を聞き　見る
すぐに遠ざかり思い出だけがあかるく残る
わたしの内に愛の源泉があるなら涸れているのに滴りはじめる
わたしの時は止まったのにゆっくり未來へ流れ出す
恐ろしい悲しみが薄れてゆくのに
喜び駆け寄ろうとするとあなたの不在に気づき立ち止まる
　どこかへいっただけ　いつもの手提げに思い出を詰めて白い
　風のなかにいる
　好きだった木陰で眠っている　花びらが散り見えないだけ
　ちょっとどこかへ出かけただけ
あおい天が広がり緑の木々や草をぬって水がきらめく
自然は　世界は変わらずに美しく幸せそうにあり
人々は生きるのに忙しく　だましたり恨んだり笑ったりしている
世界を覆そうとしてテロはあり　希望はたいてい手に入らない
大勢のひとは簡単に死ぬのに　たった一人の平和な死を悼む
不公平な世界に生かされていると心を鎮め
生かされている重みは死を待つひとには確かだ
――なにも本当のことはわからない
太鼓でも叩いて歌いたい
ひとは残酷にも天使のようにもなるのに
神々は気まぐれに悲しみだけをひとに負わせる
――本当のことはなにもわからない

Nobuko Ueki (Japan / Niigata)

Changing Sea

Where is the starting point and where is the destination?
The existence of one life is to be forgotten and buried
My memory in pieces appear one after another at random
They are so dear just like a wind: so it be
It blows down splitting the deepest sky
From spaces of green trees and dips among grasses
It also rises and comes to me hitting twigs
It goes swaying flowers and grasses
The image of my dear one start flowing like a streamer
Instantly I hear the voice and see the face
Though it is now gone far with only the image left bright
If I have a fountain of love inside me
Though it is now dried it should start dripping again
If time stops it shall slowly start flowing to the future
Terrible sadness is now fading away
Though I run toward you I suddenly stop for your absence
  You just gone somewhere: you must stand in a white wind
  Packing memories in your bag you always loved to use
  You are sleeping in the tree shade you liked
  You are invisible because falling petals screen you from me
  You just popped out somewhere
We are busy living: deceiving and cursing others or smile
We have terrorism for the purpose of overturning the world
Though we have seldom hope
Many people are killed easily while I mourn a peaceful death
Recognizing we live in this unfair world but still we have to live
It will be a heavy oppression at least to the people who are dying
That will be certain
——Anything true is unknown
Let me sing songs striking a drum!

波が寄せ　引き　循環する大気
木々の呼吸　木の葉の呼吸が光り輝いて
賛歌を歌う児が重なり並んでいっぱいだ

We can be cruel: we can be angels
Yet why do gods the whimsical burden us only with sadness?
——Anything true is unknown

Waves come and pull: the air on the earth circulates
Trees take breaths and the leaves will shine bright
So many children shall sing hymns in lines together

(Translator: Noriko Mizusaki)

秋葉信雄（日本・千葉）
Nobuo Akiba (Japan / Chiba)

Hanging Thread

Magnolia is falling down from the sky
Magnolia is falling down from the Sky

I've been telling you you were living a lie
You've been thinking of something to say good bye
I know you're lying when you're making a sigh
But you didn't quit it and fitting me cry

Some people say " She is living over you."
I say none of you don't know about her few
They say " It's gonna be alright if you'll find a new"
No it's gonna be alright while she stays my crew

While we were shipping for China yes she said
There's a place nobody knows called "Hanging Thread"
She didn't make a sigh and told me "It's time to wed."
At last I found myself dreaming in our bed

Still Doing

I forgot to bring it : everything in my heart
You forgot to bring it : just nothing in your fart
Remember to drink it : everything in your cart
Remember to think it : but nothing in your chart

Oh what could be true love everything in your junk
You spend the things above just only in your dunk
You forgot to wing doves just only to sing funk
You'd better sing in pub becoming to your drunk

You'll be happy so much if you got your medal
Your boss gave you the clutch you must push your pedal
You keep on doing fudge just only to kick kettle
Your brain is such and such you stay in your vessel

But I have to say that you're over me
And I'm still doing, yes, on bended knee

水崎野里子（日本・東京）
Noriko Mizusaki (Japan / Tokyo)

モンゴル日記：2019年5月
My Travel Diary to Mongol in May: 2019

山ならぬ空の境涯越えて来た命なりけりモンゴル再訪
Not a mountain but over the boundaries in the sky
I crossed to come: I stand in my Mongol for my life

驚きはウランバートル近代化あらよモダンのデパートスーパー
In my surprise Ulaanbaatar turned into a modern city
Modernized department stores or supermarkets here!

変わらぬは緑草原どこまでも拡がり羊ゐる陽に輝きて
Unchanged is the green steppe spreading endlessly
Look! Over there sheep grazing quiet: lit in the sun

バス降りて小高き丘の天辺にははるばる登るレストランまで
Stepping down from the bus we climbed a small hill
Up at the top we saw a tiny restaurant nice and cozy

洒落た店卓に座るも大皿に山と盛られたラム肉骨付き
So neat a place in my memory: sitting we all for lunch
On the table a heap of lamb barbecue with bones!: a lot

ジンギスカンの名前の焼肉夜食の旨し食べるばかりが旅ではなくも
Genghis Khan so called: then in the night barbecue dishes tasty though
Not only for foods we traveled: illuminated the city we saw outside bright

わが旅路かつても今も交流の国境超えたる親睦胸に
For my travels the first purpose is to be cultural exchanges
I know well and sure: putting in my bosom deep in my chest

街中のギャラリー建物堂々と若き女史二人に短歌の説明
The art gallery downtown majestic: the Japan Fair there we had
With two ladies Mongolian how Japanese tanka I spoke: it happy

終わりには大統領なる官邸で祝宴ありてもてなし感謝
In the end we were welcomed in the guest house of the Mongol president
Thankful for the ceremony and so for the party: we happy we all say now

ジンギスカンの巨大彫像山の上見上げてわれは馬上の人に
A gigantic statue of Genghis Khan on the hill lying: looking it up in the sky
To our big amazement oh! Then we walked to ride on a horse stepping grass

馬に乗る観光用のイベントよ恐怖なれどものろのろ歩き
Riding on a horse it a touring attraction I knew: though I had some frightening
At the high position upon him the horse had slow walks carrying me on the back

わが夢はモンゴル平原疾走よ馬を駆りいてどこまでも行く
My dream: on the Mongolian steppe galloping I go reining
A horse I shall dash on as far as I can to the end of the earth

英雄は侵略者であり大帝国は他民族殺害隷属　歴史矛盾は知るも言わずに
The great hero the invader: the great empire with great people
Other races oppressed: Irony of history I did not say yet I know

ジンギスカンの兜もていざやラム肉焼かむかななぜか五月人形の兜の影ある
On the iron big helmet of Genghis Khan let's barbecue lamb together
Somehow a Japanese May doll's toy helmet doubling it in the shadows

かつて今蒼き狼モンゴルに立つ
Once and now
A Blue wolf stands
Up in Mongol

(Translated by the Author)

東京百景：新宿

1.

夜深き
ネオンの街道
車のライト

新宿の
三丁目なる
交差点

夜眩し
赤信号に
われはストップ

通りの名
早稲田通りに
甲州街道

信号を
渡るとわれに
コンビニ明かり

夜学教師に
路地裏
電灯

2.

若き日の
新宿思ひ出
歩行者天国

紀伊国屋
千疋屋なる
通り人群（むれ）

京王の
デパート見上げ
地下道へ

若き人々
デートは公園
アベックベンチ

三角の
建物都庁は
空に聳えて

ピットイン
銭の無ければ
ジャズ語る

今むかし
新宿騒動
去りし過去

SHINJUKU:
——from The One Hundred Tokyo Sites (3)

(1)

It the night now
Neon-illuminated streets
Light of cars: glare

Here Shinjuku
3- chome: at the
Crossway I stand

Night shines
The red signal
Stopped me

Names of the streets:
Waseda Street this way
Koshu Highway that way

Across the cross
A convenience store
Foot- lighted me

The city lamps high
At the back street familiar
To a night school teacher

(2)

In my young days
A vivid memory of my Shinjuku
Walker Heaven was

Across Kinokuniya Bookstore
Senbikiya fruit parlor: on the street
A crowd of walkers walk packed

Looking up high the Keio
Department store you go down
To the underground route long

Young couples in the night
Having a date on the bench for lovers
In the Central Park: let's sit together

Tokyo Metropolitan Government
Office: the triangular roofs stick
Soars up to the sky of Tokyo high

Pit-In: the jazz coffee shop
Hardly any money with you
Let us talk hot on the Jazz

Once upon a time
Occurred Shinjuku riots
A past gone far now

３．

新宿の
前衛映画に
通ひし少女

初恋地獄篇
きちがいピエロに
８か１／２

甘い生活
スルース　オリビエ
新宿文化シアターか？

寺山修司に
ゴダール映画
マストロヤンニと
その名の眩し

新宿は
かつては粋な
若者ファッション

花園神社
テントで再び
芝居見物

老ひたる夫婦
いざ靴脱ぎゆき
昔の夢

今

(3)

For avant-garde cinemas
In the streets frequented to
A girl I was hot and crazy

The First Love: the Hell Edition
Pierrote Le Fou
8 et 2/1

La Dolce vita
Sluice; acted Olivier in the Shinjuku
Cultural & Art Cinema Theatre?

Shuji Terayama
Le Cinema de Godard
De Fedelico Fellini
Their names dazzling

Shinjuku
Once attracted
Smart young guys

Hanazono shrine
In the huge tent again
For the performance

An elderly couple
Removed shoes and stepped into
To have an old dream

Now again

(Translator: Noriko Mizusaki)

市原礼子（日本・大阪）

槐戸橋（さいかちど）

川のほとりに住んでいたころ
わたしは　ときどき
鬼になった

日本一汚れているといわれた川の
泥の黒く光る流れは
盛り上がり滞っている
川沿いの桜並木は満開で
桜の花びらが
川にも私にも散りかかる

黒い流れに架かる橋は
ちょっと奇妙な名前の　槐戸橋
鬼の棲む里につながる
人と鬼の渡る橋
この橋を渡る時は
ふりむいてはいけない
橋は私の後ろで崩れ始める

槐戸橋を渡ってゆき
槐戸橋を戻ってくる

土手の上では花の宴が
いつ果てるともなく続いている

Reiko Ichihara (Japan / Osaka)

Saikachi-do Bridge

When I lived by the river
Sometimes I turned into
A demon

They told me it is the most polluted river in Japan
The muds are glittering black in the water and
Swell up to block the current
Along the river cherry blossoms are out in full
Their petals are
Falling down on the river and me

A bridge spanned over the dark river is
Called Saikachi-do Bridge: a bit strange name
That means the direction for demons' door
Leading us to a demons' village
It is the one both for humans and demons
When going across it
I should not look back
Because it will start collapsing down
Just behind me

Crossing the bridge to the other side
I do come back across it to this side

On the banks a feast of the cherry blossoms
Has been held endless: without any breaks

(Translator: Noriko Mizusaki)

レクス・ヴァレンタイン（米国・ポーランド）

さらば旧友
ソネット

君　僕の　大事な奥さん　僕のこと思ってくれる
君の　整理好き　きれい好き　黄金だ
でも　そんなに大胆にならなくてもいいんだ
時々　君は　捨てすぎ　掃除　やりすぎる

僕の宝物　君には価値なんてない　屑だ
でも　僕　つらい　古い友だちとの　別れ
十年前の　オクスフォード靴　匂っても　捨てないでくれ
投球ゲーム用の横木は　重くなっちゃった　本当だ

ジャケットやベストは縮んじゃった！でも
捨てないでくれ　いなくなったら悲しいんだ
僕のゴルフクラブも　君　ガラクタだと思っても
二十年前　ゴルフに行っだ　行ったんだ

僕　目をつぶる　ゴミの山　見ないことにする
みんないなくなったら・・・君を見て　僕は微笑む

（日本語訳：水崎野里子）

(Japanese Translator : Noriko Mizusaki)

Rex Valentine (USA / Poland)

GOODBYE OLD FRIENDS
A Sonnet

Oh, Wife, dear Wife, you mean so much to me,
your tidiness and cleanness like gold,
Now, I don’t think you mean to be so bold,
but sometimes you go on a dumping spree.

My treasures are not value’ble to you,
but I don’t part with old friends very well.
What if my ten-year oxfords have a smell?
My bowling bail got heavier, it’s true.

My jacket and my vest have really shrunk!
Please don’t throw them away, I’d miss them so.
And though you think my golf clubs are just junk,
I *did* go golfing twenty years ago.

I’d better shut my eyes, not see the pile;
and when they’re gone…I’ll look at you and smile.

崔龍源（日本・東京）

鳥はうたった

一本のやせた稲の穂のために
縛られ　束ねられた手のために
飢えて　やせさらばえた子のために
頭上を翔ける鳥はうたった
もろもろの生きもののなかで
変わりやすい仮面をつけた人間の心のなかで
鳥がつばさを失わないために
水がその美しい鼓動を途絶えさせることのないために
ぼくは生きたい　と

跛行の犬の垂れた尾の下で　すでに
没落している都会を翔ける鳥はうたった
すべてを奪われる側に立つひとのために
そのかき消されてゆく声のために
ぼくは　うたいたい　と
空は　どこまでもひろがり続けるだろう
永劫の種族であるけものたちの心のなかで
確かに育っているただひとつの生
あらゆる存在をつらぬく生を
たたえるために　そのたたえられた無垢のために
ぼくは　生きたい　と

実る前に刈りとられた小麦のために
涸れ切った泉のために
骨と皮だらけの魂のために
うすばかげろうの声がみちる野や川で
太陽の額に　ぼくはぼくの存在理由をしるしたい　と
風媒花の種子を啄みながら
ユーラシアを翔ける鳥はうたった
死の灰で空を汚さないで

Ryugen Sai (Japan / Tokyo)

Song of a Bird

For the sake of a thin ear of rice plant
For the sake of hands tied up and bundled
For the sake of a thin and bony child starved
Fluttering high up in the sky a bird sang:
"In so many living creatures on the earth
In the minds of humans precarious and masked
For the sake of birds not to lose wings
For the sake of water not be deprived of beautiful pulsing
I wish to live"

Fluttering wings in the sky the bird sang the song of the city
Declined under the crippled dog with the tail drooping
"For the sake of people who take sides of the ones who would be deprived of all
For the sake of their voices which will be hushed I wish to sing:
The sky spreads out endless with no confines
Life surely to be growing up
Even in the beasts in the one of the eternal species
Life is there through all the existences
That I wish to admire and for the innocence admired
I wish to live"

For the sake of the wheat having clipped away before it ripened
For the sake of the fountain dried up
For the sake of souls all covered with bones and skins
In the fields and rivers full of the voices of ant lions
I shall wish to imprint a reason for my existence on the forehead of the sun
Pecking at the seeds of the wind medium flower
Fluttering wings in the Eurasian sky he sang:
"May you make the misery deaths not stain grasses and stones and walls

海をからっぽにしないで
銃火に子供の顔を向けないで
母の乳房を　帆のように張らせて
みじめな死を　無数のぼろぎれのような血で
草や石や壁ににじませないで
ああ明晰な道を
吹き過ぎる風でありたい　と

すべての大地を翔ける鳥はうたった
傷ついた樹々や花々のために
鳴きしげる昆虫や魚たちのかき乱された棲家のために
無数の生あるもののなかで
ひとがつばさを失わないために
水が　その美しい鼓動を途絶えさせることのないために
ぼくは　生きたい　と

（二〇一九年二月日本詩人クラブ例会にての朗読詩）

With spilled blood like a heap of raged old cloths
Oh I wish I would be a wind blowing through
On a road lighted: not dark nor any dirty"

The bird sang flying high over all lands
"For trees and flowers hurt and painful
For insects crying together and for the destroyed nests of fishes
For the sake of humans not to lose their wings
In so many living things on the earth
For thc sake of water not to be deprived of beautiful pulsing
I wish to live"

(Recited in the Japan Poets Club Monthly Meeting in February: 2019)

鎌倉佐弓（日本・埼玉）
Sayumi kmakura (Japan / Saitama)

鎌倉佐弓俳句集（1）

木枯らしにゆれる一葉に夕日の輪

Tha halo of a setting sun
around a leaf
shaking in the winter wind

菜の花の黄に染むシャツをふり洗ひ

A shirt dyed the yellow
of the rape flower——
I shake and wash it

わが未来までは行かずに紅葉山

I don’t visit
until my future——
Momijiyama

裏門に声を残して卒業す

Leave your voice
at the rear gate——
my graduation

空を見る計画もあり夏の旅

I have a plan
to see the sky, too——
a summer journey

わが行方我が作りたし鰯雲

My whereabouts
want to create me——
the cirrocumulus

くぼめるは何を忘れし冬帽子

What did it forget
to make itself so hollow?
The winter hat

芽吹く樹に凭れひとりの透きとほる

Leaning back
on a budding tree
I'm transparent

Translator : James Shea

Scott Watson (USA / Japan / Miyagi)
スコット・ワトソン（米国 / 日本 / 宮城）

The Home Front
銃後

by Taneda Santōka
種田山頭火

Introduced and translated by
Scott Watson
和十尊歌

2018

草木塔 (Sōmokutō, Grass Tree Cairn) appeared in April of the 15th year of Shōwa (1940), the same year he died (October). It is Santōka's major work. 701 free-style haiku appear in it, though I myself have not counted them. Those 701 poems are grouped under 11 headings. One of those headings is "The Home Front," and there are twenty-five haiku under that heading. It is the smallest group of poems in the collection.

My interest in the theme of Santōka and war began when, maybe ten years ago, I read an English translation of the short novel introduced below. In the years prior to that, reading, translating, and in general learning about Santōka, he never came across as someone who might have been a right wing hawk.

In 1975 Japanese author and literary critic Maruya Saiichi published a short novel with the title **横しぐれ** (an English translation appeared in 1990 with the title **Rain in the Wind**). In that story appears a character named Santōka who is based on the real life Santōka but who has been depicted as a right-wing hawkish imperialist. In that story, some of Santōka's actual diary entries and some of his poems from "The Home Front" are interpreted as support for Japan's imperialist war of aggression.

Granted the interpretation of poetry is——when not a matter of community consensus——subjective, granted the story is a work of fiction, granted freedom of expression, to me the story in an undignified way exploits a very fine poet's name ——though Santōka definitely had his share of shortcomings——for some reason I cannot understand. Just to sell a story? Had this happened in America, someone in the Taneda family likely would have brought a lawsuit against Mr. Maruya. But Japan is not America; it's not nearly as litigious.

At the time Santōka made those poems, Japan was under militarist rule. The powers that be were doing a good job controlling the hearts and minds of the populace, gearing the entire nation for war. Their tentacles reached everywhere, from mass communications to classrooms to neighborhood organizations to women's groups to farmers' organizations to religious organizations. From birth to death, Japanese in Japan could not escape war fervor. It was one big never ending rallying of spirit and effort.

Given that scene, it would be remarkable if Santōka were not, as Maruya claims he was in his story, connected to right wing elements. Right wing was everywhere, everything, on the surface, or publicly. Japan's entire population was, outwardly at least, a right wing hawkish element. Anyone not was either in prison or dead.

Opposition to war was not tolerated. Santōka was not openly opposed to war, but he saw through all its glorification. He realized war means gore. In diaries he writes that even though he thinks war is inevitable for the human animal, it means misery and is detestable. Reading newspaper articles about the war, he found them depressing even though the articles themselves were excitedly telling of the imperial army's conquests. He knew his attitude would be viewed as unpatriotic. The sadness he felt about war, for this man who was already emotionally unstable and susceptible to suicidal bouts of depression, likely lead him, with an overdose of sleeping potion, to another attempt to take his own life.

Maruya must have missed those diary entries. The following poems are his response not so much to war itself (battles, fighting, etc.)——he wrote in a diary that war poems are shallow——but to war's effect on a scene he himself could witness, on those back home in Japan, the home front. I don't see how, unless someone really strains, any of them can be interpreted as supporting any war effort. Although they are not openly anti-war, which (writing antiwar
poems), would have further jeopardized Santōka's already fragile existence as an outsider in Japanese society then, they penetrate to the essence of all war anywhere, any time.

Here is one of the poems Maruya sets forth as supporting war:

月のあかるさはどこを爆撃してゐることか

Light of the moon——
does it know
where bombs
kaboom?

Even though I take some liberty with the almost nonsensical use of "kaboom," the spirit is there.

It seems to me that, as is the case with countless Santōka poems, he sees nature as going on regardless of our human world with its various ambitions and endeavors. Nature doesn't care about us——we humans obviously don't care awfully much about us either. If we did, we wouldn't so senselessly destroy everything.

Despite our attempts to separate ourselves from nature's way, we inevitably, inescapably, return to it.

Let us go, then, to the home front.

THE HOME FRONT

天われを殺さずして詩を作らしむ
われ生きて詩を作らむ
われみづからのまことなる詩を
Heaven don’t let me be killed let me make poems
Let me live to make poems
My own life’s true poems

街頭所見 Street Scenes

日ざかりの千人針の一針づつ
High noon’s
1000 stitch belt’s*
1 stitch at a time

*1000 stitch belt: worn as an amulet by soldiers.
https://en.m.wikipedia.org/wiki/Senninbari

月のあかるさはどこを爆撃してゐることか
Light of the moon——
does it know
where bombs
kaboom?

秋もいよいよふかうなる日の丸へんぽん
Deeper
and deeper
autumn
Rising Sun* flutters

*Rising Sun: Japan's national flag

ふたたびは踏むまい土を踏みしめて征く
Never again to tread this land
march off to conquer another

しぐれて雲のちぎれゆく支那をおもふ
Drizzling* clouds sunder thinking of China

* Drizzling: refers to late autumn / early winter drizzle. These poems were composed during the Second Sino-Japanese War. Japan had not yet attacked Pearl Harbor.

戦死者の家 Home of a Fallen Soldier

ひつそりとして八ツ手花咲く
Inconspicuously fatsia flowers blossom

*Fatsia Japonica (it has other English names such as a paper plant) is a flowering plant native to Japan. It blooms (white flowers) in winter, which——late autumn/early winter——is when these poems were made. Its glossy leaves resemble an outspread hand. It Japan's language of flowers it is said to communicate (without words) a sense of separation, or friendliness, or health. Another way to pronounce the Japanese would be "hasshu," which sounds something like English "hush."

遺骨を迎ふ Receiving Ashes (of dead soldiers)

しぐれつつしづかにも六百五十柱
Autumn drizzle hush
six-hundred-fifty
dead.

もくもくとしてしぐるる白い函をまへに
Without a word
early winter drizzle
carry a white box*

> *Boxes containing ashes of dead soldiers, were often carried home by a family member from an arranged place of transfer (i.e. a train station or wharf). The plain, unfinished, paulownia boxes were wrapped in a white cloth that could be draped over shoulders to support the box's weight. Inside a box was a white porcelain urn within which were cremation's remains: ashes and bone bits. They were carried by hand in front at heart/abdominal level. We might imagine there was ceremony involved, with maybe a veterans' military band playing something suiting the notion of heroic death. Those witnessing the event would have their heads lowered. See the cover photo.

山裾あたたかなここにうづめます
Bury in warm mountain skirts

凩の日の丸二つ二人も出してゐる
Winter wind's two Rising Suns for two sons*

> *The original reads "two persons." It might be a father and a son, or two brothers. Two from the same home are in the war.

冬ぼたんほつと勇ましいたよりがあつた
Winter tree peony
relieved with news
of bravery

雪へ雪ふる戦ひはこれからだといふ
Snow falling on snow
battle about to come

勝たねばならない大地いつせいに芽吹かうとする
All over this vast land that must have victory
all at once buds open

遺骨を迎へて Receiving Ashes

いさましくもかなしくも白い函
In valor
in sorrow
in a white box

街はおまつりお骨となつて帰られたか
A town in festival
their sons now bones
come back home

遺骨を抱いて帰郷する父親
Holding dearly [a son's]
ashes a father
returns home

ぽろぽろしたたる汗がましろな函に
In large drops sweat drips on a pure white box

お骨声なく水のうへをゆく
Bones with no voice move upon water

その一片はふるさとの土となる秋
That one bit*
become hometown soil
autumn

*of bones/ashes

みんな出て征く山の青さのいよいよ青く
Off to conquer.
Mountain green
greener still.

馬も召されておぢいさんおばあさん
Horses must go too,
grandmother, grandfather

ほまれの家 House of Honor

音は並んで日の丸はたたく
Side by side
sounds of
Rising Sun
flapping.

* A home of a fallen soldier received imperial designation as "House of Honor" (誉の家). A plaque inscribed with "House of Honor" was placed at the entrance. Plaques were made of iron, wood, or aluminum and were apparently at one time coated with gold flake, which would wear off in time. Metal plaques disappeared as the war went on because metals were needed for the war effort.

歓送 Hearty Send-off (going off to war)

これが最後の日本の御飯を食べてゐる、汗
Partaking of this
last repast*
perspiration.

*Last meal in Japan

ぢつと瞳が瞳に喰ひ入る瞳
Steadily vision engages vision

* the original uses “hitomi” which means an eye’s pupil but can also be thought of as a more poetic way of saying eye.

案山子もがつちり日の丸ふつてゐる
Scarecrow too
stands straight
waving of the flag

戦傷兵士 War Casualties

足は手は支那に残してふたたび日本に
Arms and legs left in China once more in Japan

Translator's Note

This project has been different in nature than my other endeavors to bring Santōka into English. That is because these Home Front poems require more understanding of a particular time in Japanese history. For example I had to learn about funerary customs in Japan in the 1930s and for Japanese military in particular. Help with that learning process came from a dear friend. I am grateful to Ms. Yuko Takada for her assistance.

Scott Watson
万流庵

All-Flowing Cottage
Sendai, Japan
October, 2018

お母さん
ありがと

梁瀬重雄（日本・埼玉）

正月　四

額に留めどなく溢れる涙と汗を
いくら大地に流しても
そこに川が生まれるわけではないが

滝のように流れ落ちる涙と汗は
土を抱えて生きる　百姓の
豊作の祈りの言葉が
しがみついていることを
大地はよく知っている

今年も　わたしは
大粒の涙と汗と夢を
太陽の温もりの踊る大地に
追憶の子守り唄をうたうように
何度も繰り返し流すだろう

涙と汗と夢の　憩う
新しい朝がやって来る
ほんとうの夜がやって来る
そんな静かな野辺の大地に……

Shigeo Yanase (Japan / Saitama)

On a New Year's Day 4

Tears and sweats endlessly gather
On my forehead: even if I let them flow
Down on the earth it is not that
They would turn into a river

Though the earth knows well that
The tears and sweats cascading
Are closely linked with the prayer
For a rich harvest
Prayed by farmers: who live on soil

This year again I shall brim down
The large teardrops and sweats and dreams
Onto the earth: where the warm sun shall dance
So many times repeatedly
Just like I sing a lullaby far in my memory

When a fresh morning should come on to us
So should a true night do
When farmers can take their rest
On such a calmed land on the earth ……

(Translator: Noriko Mizusaki)

作土

先祖が大事に耕して来た　農地だから
作土の土は滑らかで柔らかく
作物は根をどこまでもはり大空に伸びる

ここで働く農家はみな土色の顔
麦藁帽子を被り
どんな髯づらの顔をしていても
それを隠す一本の手拭いがあればいい

野良着すがたのぼくを作土は笑顔で迎え
憎悪をはらむどんな風雪にも耐えながら
しっとりと可憐な花の咲く日が
やってくる季節をいつも待っている

春の作物　夏の作物
秋の作物　冬の作物　を
武将の心のように何のこだわりもなく育てる
これが先祖が大事にして来た　命の農地

作土は何度　馬に踏まれ風雨に傷付いても
けっして猪のような牙を向けない
慈雨を信じ逆襲することもなく
いくたの試練に耐え
発酵熟成され滑らかな柔らかい土になる

農産物を輸入し
この豊穣な作土を粗末にする社会
お前のどす黒い血がぼくの骨まで洗い
お前の欲望の差し伸ばす黒い手首が
影絵のようにぼくの背筋を這いのぼる

作土は細かい目で広い空間を緑につつみ

Soil Cultivated

Our ancestors plowed the soil of the field
Smooth and soft: so that plants may take
Roots as they like to grow up to the sky

Farmers have faces in a color of the soil
Here; they wear straw hats on the heads
When they would have beards unshaved
They can cover them with their facecloths

The soil smiles to me in my working jacket
Enduring weathers malicious and hostile
It is always waiting for the season to come
When lovely flowers bloom and open gentle

The harvest in the spring: the one in the summer
In the autumn and in the winter: on a large mind
I have cultivated any of them with no partiality
For ancestors cherished the soil of fields so dear

It was stepped on by horses and was hurt by storms
Though it never turned fangs on us: not as wild boars
Believing the merciful rain: not having counterattacks
It has endured silently so many hard and rough trials
Fermented and ripened it becomes smooth and soft

Import the agricultural products: it's the officials' policy
In it they do not think as valuable the soil so dear to me
Their black blood would wash even my bones and flesh
They stretching me their black hands polluted in avarice
Angry would go crawling up on my back: in my nightmare

The large space wrapped in green: having given us the

血と汗の滲む作土は穀物の豊穣をもたらし
いつの世も人々の飢えを救っていたのに
紙屑のように吹雪の中へ放り出され
積雪に残る幽かな足跡まで消して行くのだ

Rich harvest of corns undergoing through hardest trials
The soil had always saved us from hunger: I wish they
May not throw it away like a waste into the snowstorm
It will erase out the smallest footprints barely left to us

(Translator: Noriko Mizusaki)

原詩夏至（日本・東京）
Shigeshi Hara (Japan / Tokyo)

ミサイル
On a Missle and Other Tanka Poems

「俺はもう俺の無垢など信じてはいない」血の手を拭き青年は
"I cannot believe your innocence any more"
Wiping the blood of the hands said a young man

君ももう君の無垢など信じてはいない水子の墓いま後に
You also do not believe your innocence yourself
Now you turn from the grave of a miscarried child

ロックオンしたミサイルが音速の君を追う俺など置き去りに
A missile locked on flies after sonic you
Leaving me behind

シャッターが起爆装置で皆爆死したあの夏の記念撮影
A shutter was a detonator that exploded to kill all
The commemorative photo on the summer

漕いでいる又はあえなく流されている月光の筏海まで
Rowing a raft——or being forced into drifting?——
——Floating down to the sea in the moonlight

（「まろにゑ50号記念誌）より）
From the Poetry Magazine Marronnier :#50;
In the Celebration Issue of the 50th Publication

(Translator: Shigeshi Hara & Noriko Mizusaki)

浦島

浦島は　もう死んでいたのだ
本当は　もう死んでいたのだ
本当は　乙姫は龍だし
龍宮に　到着して早々
浦島は　クスリで眠らされて
頭から　食われてしまったのだ
カメは　最初からそのつもりで
龍宮に　浦島を拉致したのだ
カメを　苛めていた子供たちは
本当は　ヤラセのサクラなのだ
浦島が　釣った魚の子供たちが
本当は　ヒトに化けていたのだ
復讐のため？
生活のため？
娯楽のため？
分からない
分からないが
恐らくは
その全部だったんだろう

浦島は　もう死んでしまった
なのに　浦島の「夢」は　生き残った
親切が　いつか報われるという「夢」
楽園が　どこかにあるという「夢」
タイや　ヒラメの舞い踊る「夢」
平凡な　馬鹿な男の見る「夢」
馬鹿な　水泡の歓楽の「夢」

浦島は　馬鹿な男だから
三百年　自分の死を知らなかった
三百年　馬鹿な「夢」を見続けて
三百年　海底に沈んでいた

死体は　とうに白骨と化しても
妄執の　酒池肉林の「夢」に
三百年　成仏できなかった

なのに　或る時　浦島は気づいた
全てが　あまりに容易すぎることに
全てが　あまりに楽しすぎることに
人生が　もし　これだけのものなら
所詮は　そんなもの「夢」と同じだ
何百年　続けても無意味なのだ

浦島は　「生きたい！」と思った
地上で　地に足をつけ生きたい！
故郷の　あの　貧しい漁師町で！
浦島は　乙姫に訴えた
沢山だ　もうこんな生活！
復活だ　俺は生まれ変わるのだ！
水泡の　浮草の日々から
いっそ　もう足を洗いたいのだ！

乙姫は　艶然と笑った
浦島に　心で呼びかけた
あのね　浦島さん　洗おうにも
私たち　足なんかないのよ
だって　私は　最初から龍だし
貴方は　もう　とっくに幽霊だし
だけど　私も　最後くらいは
貴方に　見せなくちゃね　せめてもの真心を
念の為　後腐れがないように……

乙姫は　玉手箱を渡した
浦島は　勇躍　帰郷した
そして　忽ち　「真実」に気づいた
故郷は　もはや異郷に過ぎないこと
しかも　龍宮には　もう戻れぬこと

自分に　居場所など　もうないこと
そして　ただ一つ　残った　玉手箱

そこに　最後に匿われた「追憶」
それは　誰にも奪えない筈だった
浦島は　とうとう　玉手箱を開けた
けれど　中には「追憶」などではなく
最後の　究極の「真実」が詰まっていた
浦島が　もう　とっくの昔に
死んで　この世にないという「真実」が……

白煙が　渚の風に　消えたとき
白髪の　浦島など　いなかった
浦島は　どこにも　いなかった
白煙が　つまりは　浦島だった
浦島の　死ねない　「夢」が今
ついに　成仏して　消えたのだ

消えた　白煙
白煙が　消えたこと
消えた　浦島
浦島が　消えたこと

それが　浦島の
最後の　救いだった……

（2019年8月17日「パンドラ詩の朗読会」にて朗読：於東京・神田）

松尾静明(ゆうき　あい/ 日本・広島)

組曲『ヒロシマ』
第二章　「天も地も燃えた日に」より(2)

川の水がうずまき、水の柱が立っていました。

川の中の筏は、死んだひと、死ぬひとの体でシートのように覆われ浮き沈みしていました。

川には、つぎつぎとひとが飛び込み、あるひとたちは、手をつないで川下へ流れていきました。水の色は血と灰がまざって醬油の色をしておりました。

何頭もの馬が倒れて、もがき、鳴いていて、そこへも火が移り、毛皮が燃えあがりました。

電車が何人ものひとを乗せたまま燃え、それはやがて黒い弁当箱のような形になりました。

「水をちょうだい！」と叫ぶ少女がいました。空の水筒を見せながら走り抜けました。

わたしは逃げました。たくさんの助けを求める声をふりきって、わたしは逃げました。
わたしは逃げました。

コールタールのにおいのする黒い色の雨が降ってきて、それが建物の燃えるにおいと、ひとの焼けるにおいを少しやわらげましたが、またひとの焼けるにおいがたちこめました。

皮膚が焼けてむけた母親のそばに、やはり焼けた女の子がいて、その子は「アマアマ」と言って母親の乳房を求めていましたが、母親はもう動きませんでした。

Seimei Matsuo (Japan / Hiroshima)

From the Second Chapter: in the Hiroshima Suite On the Day when the Heaven the Earth Burned (2)

The River was whirling around and the kind of water columns rising up.

In the water I was floating on, together with the dead and dying ones, all packed around me.

Citizens jumped into the river, one after another. Some of them were drifted down the river, holding hands each other. The color of the river looked like soy source, mixed with blood and ashes.

Horses fell down on the ground. They struggled, neighing. Fire was blown to fall upon them to scorch their furs.

Trains burned up with the passengers in. They turned into something like black lunch boxes.

"Give me water!" shouting, a girl was running through, with her empty water bottle.

I escaped. I escaped, not taking any cares for calling voices for my help.
I escaped.

The black rain came down falling on us, smelling of coal tar. It absorbed for some time the smell of the burning houses and humans. But again it started to fill the air.

One woman lied on the ground with the burned skin peeled off. Beside her, I saw a little girl, who was also burned. She was crying for mother's breast milk, but her mother did not move.

女学生たちが逃げながら話していました。「うちはもう動けん」「みんなはどうしたのじゃろうか」「うちはもう目が見えんよ」「うちはお母さんに会いたい」「みんなで呼ぼうよ」「おかあさん、おかあさん、おかあさん」

男の子たちはみな半分裸で、肩や腕の皮はぶらさがっていました。顔は真っ赤でした。それは皮膚が焼けて下の骨の所まで見えていたからです。

どこからか「君が代」が聞こえてきました。土手の上へ立っている者も、地面から立てない者も、うたい始めました。まっ黒い大合唱でした。

川岸の石段に中学生たちが黒く焦げて段々に折り重なって、それは石炭袋のように見えました。岸辺には、まだ食べていない弁当箱がふたがとれて飛び散り、ごはんが焦げていました。

Escaping the girl students, crying each other; "I cannot move any loner," "What became of others?" "I cannot see!" " I want to see my mother!" "Let's call her together!" "Mother! Mother! Mother!"

Boys were half naked. Their skins were hanging down, on the shoulders and on the arms. Their faces looked all red. Their skins of faces were all burned and we could see the flesh and bones, the part under them.

I heard singing voices of the Japanese anthem, from somewhere. The ones standing on the bank and the ones who could not rise up again, all those ones had started singing. It had turned into a big chorus.

On the stone steps on the river side, the middle high school students were piled in a heap, one upon another, all burned black, They looked like, as if they had been black coals in a coal sack. There, the covers had flown away from the lunch boxes, I saw the rice inside, not eaten, all scorched black.

(Translator: Noriko Mizusaki)

第三章　みらいはどこ？

みらい

みらい　と名づけた
生まれて六か月で逝(い)った　おんなの子
はだしで白い砂浜を走り
草いきれのなかを転(まろ)び
野茨の白い花に　清らかなものを想い
誰かと出会って
ということもなく

ついに　ことばを覚えなかった　みらい
笑いは覚えた　みらい
怒りは覚えなかった　みらい
ひとのかたちをして　ひとにはなれなかった　みらい

初めての血　を怖れるということもなく
おんなのかたちをして　女にはなれなかった　みらい

みらい
いまここに　ちいさく横たわっている
もの　のような

みらい
我々を　はげしく　不安にさせ　怖れさせ
ひざまづかせる

みらい
時間の流れなど持たなかったのに
確かにここに名づけられて
みらい

The Third Chapter: Where is Future Gone?

You: for FUTURE

I name you FUTURE
A girl baby who passed away in six months old
You could
Not Run through on a white beach barefooted
Not tumble down in a strong smell of the summer grass
Not think of something clear seeing white blossoms of the brier
Not meet someone you loved

You could not memorize words at all
You knew how to laugh but
You did not know how to get angry
You could not live as a human: having the figure

You had no fear of the first blooding of women's
You could not live as a woman: having the figure

You
Like something
Before us lying in a small figure

You
Give us terrible worries and fears
Have us always kneel down

You
Had no stream of a lifetime: Yet
Surely I name you now
As Future

(Translator: Noriko Mizusaki)

志田静枝（日本・大阪・長崎）

七夕

となり街の駅で
ひらひらと短冊が舞っている
ああ　七夕が近づいたのね
もう子どもたちも手をはなれ
笹に吊るす事も無くなり
それでも吊るされた色紙が

私を呼ぶ
笹の葉に色とりどりの
夢を掴むように私は
短冊に書かれた文字を読む
一枚の短冊には
彼女のデブが治りますように

ふっと　ふき出した私の心
若いっていいなあ……
私は八十歳のおばあさん
秋には八十一歳……でもね
歳を重ねても日々楽しいよ
それはね……秘密なの……

Shizue Shida (Japan / Osaka / Nagasaki)

Star Festival

In the station of the next town
Strips of colored paper flutters in the wind
Oh! The star festival is coming again
My children have grown up to adults
They got out of the ages for the festival
Though hanging strips of colored paper

Appeal to me
As if I were catching the colored dreams
In so many colors written on the bamboo leaves
I go read their prayers one after another
On the one a child wrote:
"May her fatness be cured"

I happened to burst out laughing
How nice childhood is …..
I am an old lady at the age of eighty
In the next autumn becoming eighty one…Yet
Getting aged year by year I enjoy my days
How? …it….a secret…you know

(Translator: Noriko Mizusaki)

夢に咲く花

はかない夢と知りながら
踏み入った道は
言葉を紡ぎだす詩の世界であった
この道四十年は長かったけれど
まだまだ続く　悔いはない
明日も　あさっても
果てしなく続く道に
その先にどんな花が咲き私に
見せてくれるのか楽しみだ
赤い花
白い花
黄色い花か
それとも私の好きな薄紫の花か
夢に咲く花の色はしばし私を
夢中にさせる

Flowers in My Dream

Knowing it an impossible dream
I stepped into a way
To the world of poetry for spinning words out
Forty years of my career was long to me yet
I shall continue to go on the way with no regrets
Tomorrow and the day after tomorrow as well
The way endlessly going on
In the end what flowers will bloom to show me?
I am looking forward to seeing them
Red ones?
White ones?
Yellow ones?
Or light purple flowers I like?
What colors of them in my dream
For some time makes me exciting

(Translator: Noriko Mizusaki)

安森ソノ子（日本・京都）

国連本部を訪れて

地雷は　目の前に
丸い形　だいだい色の兵器は展示されていて
対人地雷と聞き　見つめ続ける
話で頭に入っていた地雷は　こういう形か

踏んだ者を爆破　殺傷する物体は
人を殺すというより
大変な負傷をおわせる兵器
戦乱後の地で　土の中に多くひそんでいる今

この恐ろしさを内包して
地球は回っている
撤去の運動が善意の歩みで進んでいても
土中に眠る破壊力は
どのような内なる言葉を持つのか

予測という＜不吉な展開＞
敵の通過が予測される場所に設置
人が踏むと重さで反応
起爆装置についているもの　ワイヤーが
引っぱられたり　振動や生じる傾斜に反応

ニューヨークの国連本部を訪れ
体に埋まった地雷の姿
全世界に約一億一千万個の地雷が埋まっているという情報に
マンハッタンでの午後は　震えの時間と化していく

Sonoko Yasumori (Japan / Kyoto)

A Visit to the United Nations

The land mine in front of me,
Is round and of orange color.
I watch the weapon in exhibition intently which can give,
Bodily and fatal wounds to one who steps on it.
I now realize the real shape of the mine.

The weapon blows up anybody who steps on it.
Rather than killing men, its effect is more grievous,
Than death; the wounded sufferers' pain lasts for ages.
A number of mines are still under ground long after the war.

The earth turns around still.
These terrible weapons under ground although,
Campaign for removal of them are on the way by volunteers.
What are the words of the sleepers in the ground?

"The ill-omened unfolding" as Estimate.
Mines are set where the enemy army are expected to pass.
They react the weight of steps.
They also react to quakes.
Their triggering devices are so delicate.

Visiting the United Nations in New York,
I felt my own body is filled with mines.
The fact is that about 110 million mines are still asleep in the earth.
The information made me shudder with fear in the afternoon of Manhattan.

第五回国際女性会議に参加して

2019の春には、世界の女性達の真剣な活動を身近に見聞をしていた。第五回国際女性会議に参加、東京で三月二十三、二十四日に行われた当会議での体験は貴重なものとなっている。

執筆活動を若い頃より行ってきた中で、約四十年前から、国際ペンクラブの世界大会等に参加してきた。日本代表団の一人として私も一九九十年代からは日英語で自作詩の発表を続け、近年では着物姿で自作詩と共に日本の芸能、舞踏をも発表している。

一九八八年から発足している“Women's Messages”という会に所属しており、有志で時事英語を勉強している最中、当会の代表者・高嶋紀子氏と共に出席した。幸いにも取材班としての参加であった。

主催は日本の外務省。基調講演は招かれて初来日をされたノーベル平和賞の受賞者・マララ・ユスフザイ氏が担当された。

マララ女史は、現在オックスフォード大学で学んでおられる。若い強靭な意志から伝わるマララ女史の講演内容に参加者は息を呑んだ。「二十一世紀の現在も、学校へ行けない子供が如何に多いか、特に女子の教育を受ける権利に目を向け、女子教育への投資の必要、ジェンダーギャップの解体、女性の就職への応援、難民キャンプにいる女性達へ投資により先端技術を届ける事ができないか」など話が続いた。マララ女史はノーベル賞を受賞後、マララ募金の制度を父親と共に設立し、若い女性に質の高い教育を受ける権利をと、社会貢献に力を尽くしておられる。

翌日の三月二十四日には分科会も行われた。「家族の未来、頼る、活かす、分かち合う」と題する分科会で、マララ女史の父親・ジアウッディン・ユスフザイ氏が出演。パネリストの一人として「家族・社会」を中心とする話の中で持論を言及。母国で十八年間教師をしてきた経験から、子供には幼い頃からの教育が大切である点を述べられ、母国での家父長的なしきたりを自ら改めるべく、男性であっても出来る家事は行いつつある事などを、具体的に話された。

講演時間の終了後、英語で「日本の京都に住んでいる安森ソノ子です」と短い挨拶をし、会話の時間をもつ事も少し出来た。私も教師として働いてきたので共鳴する点、子育てを通しての持論などを述べた後、スナップ写真にも快く応じて下さり、予期せぬ時間となった。

Attending the Fifth World Assembly for Women

I observed women's serious activities in the world in the spring, 2019.
It was a valuable experience to attend the Fifth World Assembly for Women which was held on 23rd ans 24th in March in Tokyo.
I've been a member of the P.E.N. Club for 40 years and have been writing since my young days.
Since 1990s, I have been reading poems in English at assemblies as a member of delegation.
Also danced Japanese dance in Kimono or Japanese traditional clothes.
I also belong to "Women's Messages" organization which started in 1988 and studying current English.
I attended the Assembly with Ms. Noriko Takashima who is the representative of "Women's Messages."
The Assembly is sponsored by the Ministry of Foreign Affairs. The keynote address was made by Ms. Malala Yousafzai, who was awarded a Nobel Peace Prize.
Ms. Malala Yousafzai is studying at Oxford University.
The audience was impressed by her youthful, meaningful speech. She said, "Many children can't go to school even now."
And emphasized education for women in particular.
She talked about sexual discrimination, investment in the education for women and possibility of teaching women high technology at refugee camps.
She started the collection of contribution to give better education to women.
She, on the whole, is trying to make a great contribution to women.
And then they held a section meeting on 24th, March which is titled "Future of Family: Getting Support, Utilizing and Sharing"
Her father Mr. Ziauddin Yousafzai, gave a speech on families and society.
He is experienced in teaching for 18 years in his mother country and insisted on the early childhood education is important. He also denied patriarchy and does some housework.
After the congress, I got an opportunity to talk to him and introduced myself.
We had a chat and took a photo of ourselves.
Mr. Shinzo Abe, Prime Minister of Japan, explained the purpose of the

この会議では冒頭に安倍晋三首相により開催の趣旨が述べられ、閉会の折、首相夫人によるスピーチがあった。世界の国々で現在大変活躍中の女性達が登壇され、見事な活躍の展開を心に刻む事が出来た。ヨーロッパで活躍中の現外相(女性)、南米の国の副大統領を経た政治家、スーダンの若く美しい姿の指導者、そして女性としての全発言者の落ちついた話し方、それぞれの分野で著しい実績を上げておら女性は、日本の方々も含めて何と人を魅了するオーラーの持ち主である事か。「女性たちが輝く社会」へより前進し、男女共に人としての希求をもとに、人類が強い絆で活動できる事を願ってやまない。

Assembly at the opening. Ms. Akie Abe, Spouse of Prime Minister, Shinzo Abe, gave a closing speech.
After the explanation by the Prime Minister, active women in the world gave speeches.
Those were quite impressive. For example the female Minister of Foreign Affairs in Europe who plays an active part in the political world.
An ex-vice-premier from South America, who is a young and beautiful political leader in Sudan, talked calmly.
They get remarkable results and even have aura. Now, women are making an advance towards a glorious society.
I’d like to propose both sexes join forces and, let’s mark one of the great steps in our movement to have true happiness.

(Translated by the author)

秋田高敏（日本・千葉・富里）

たからもの

聞かないでください
尋ねないでください
あなたのたからものなんて
そんな物有りっこないし
捜しても見つかりっこ無いのですから

でももし有るとしたらなんだろう
持っている人達より持っていないけど
持っていない人達より持っている
そんな物が私のたからものなら

朝昼夜と家族と粗餐を食べ微笑み
いつとなく小鳥が周りに訪れ来ては
さえずる古びた家一軒と
舗装道をきしませながら
走行する中古車一台
クリーニング店に出し入れしては
幾度も幾度も着服している式服一着
ささやかながら衣食住に恵まれ
かけがえのない命を支え続けている
この自然と人間関係と社会こそが
私にとっては途方もない宝物なのかも知れない

では地球のたからものってなんだろう
世界人類すべての人達の
たからもってなんだろう
木々の緑と紅葉と空の青さと白い雲
鳥が群れ魚が泳ぎ蝶が舞い
澄んだ大気に清い水
テロや紛争や戦争のない平和な世界

Takatoshi Akita (Japan / Chiba / Tomizato)

Treasures

Don’t ask me please,
Don’t question to me about your treasures.
I suppose there are not such things on the earth.
If searching for them, you will not find them out.

However if I should happen to have them, what are they?
Though having less than those who having many,
Having more than those who having less,
I have my own treasures at my hand.

Each day three meals I have with my family smiling.
I have an old house around which,
Little birds come visit to chirp.
I have an old second –hand car which go running,
Squeaking on the paved roads.
I have a black suit for ceremonies which I wore repeatedly,
Taking it to a laundry shop to launder, repeatedly, in and out.
Blessed with happy daily lives, though not gorgeous,
I have been sustaining my life so precious.
Nature, human relationships and my society,
They might be the treasures for me, so much precious.

Then, what is the treasure for the earth?
What is the treasure for all the people in the world?
They might be: green trees, colored leaves, the blue sky and white clouds.
Birds flocking, fish swimming and butterflies dancing,
Clear air and clear water. And it might be the peaceful world,
Free from terrorism, conflicts and wars.
Free from discriminations to races, nations,
And the world free from any poverty.

人種や民族や貧困のない自由な世界

宝物ってなんだろう
すべての人達の宝物ってなんだろう
私を含めた誰もが
あなたのあなた達の私達の宝物を
心ないハンマーで壊してはいけない
偽装した鍵で盗んではいけない
もしあなたの宝物はと聞かれたら
微笑みながら即答出来るためにも

What is the treasure?
What is the treasure for us all?
Anyone, including me, should not destroy each other's treasures
with a violent hammer.
We should not steal them with a forged key.
In order that you can answer the question quickly and smiling,
In the case when you are asked what your treasures are.

(Translator: Nobuo Akiba & Noriko Mizusaki)

きしもとタロー（日本・京都）
Taro Kishimoto (Japan / Kyoto)

「きく」を、こえていく

ずいぶん昔のことになる。とある幼稚園を訪ねた際、園長先生からとても興味深い話を聞かされた。赴任したての若い頃、子供たちを引き連れて山に登った時に、「さぁ、どんな音が聞こえてくるかな」と子供たちに尋ねたところ、子供たちは「鳥の声がする」「風が鳴ってる」というふうに、誰一人として「〜が聞こえる」といった表現を使わなかったというのだ。中には「お腹で山の音が鳴っている」、というような言い方をする子までがいたという。

もしかしたら、「音を聞く器官は、耳である」ということを大人が教え込まなければ、子供たちは「音を、耳という器官で聞こうとする」訳ではないのかも知れない。「音を感じる器官は、耳である」というのは、大人の思い込みかも知れない。そんなふうに考えて、園長先生はその後「音は耳で聞くもの」というイメージを子供たちに植え付けないよう、言葉使いには慎重になったそうだ。

世間では音楽的な能力を言い表す際に、「耳が良い・悪い」という表現がよく使われている。一方、料理の能力を表す際に、「口が良い・悪い」という表現は普通使わない。「口が良い・悪い」は、言葉使いやものの言い方の良し悪しを指し、味の判別能力や料理の腕の良し悪しは、普通「舌が良い・悪い」を使う。口は食べ物の入り口ではあるけれど、その食べ物を味わうのは舌であり、味表現の良し悪しを決定するのは、更にその奥にある何かであろう。音や音楽の入り口は耳かも知れないけれど、それらが届く鼓膜も、更にその奥にある何かも、目に見えるものではない。

僕たちは、どのように世界を認知し、また感じているのか。俗に五官・五感と言うが、耳や鼓膜が機能的に優れている人が、音や音楽を人一倍味わっているとは限らないし、視力の高い人が、出来事やものごと、目の前の人や社会全体を人一倍観察できているとは限らない。恐らく、味覚や嗅覚、触覚に関しても同じことが言える。それぞれの器官の身体的機能の高さ低さと、それらを認知する能力、それらを感じ味わう能力の高さ低さが、比例する訳ではない。物理的に五官の優れた人間が、日頃から世界を人一倍深く味わって暮らしているとは限らない。歳を重ね、視力が落ち、耳が遠くなった後に、若い頃には見えなかったものが見えてきたり、感じられていなかったことが感じられるようになることもあるだろう。

さて、音楽の世界には「合奏」という言葉がある。合奏の際には互いの音をよく聞かなくてはならないが、実は互いの音をしっかり聞いているだけでは、良い合奏にはならない。聞いているつもりでも、それだけでは互いの音が「交じり合わない」のだ。そもそも日常的に「聞く・聴く」を明確に使い分けている人は少ない。簡単に区別すると、意識的に「きく」場合には「聴く」が使われ、音や音楽が勝手に耳に入って来る場合や、人の声や話を普通にきいている場合には、「聞く」が使われる。意識的に能動的にきく場合は「聴く」が使われる訳だけれど、たとえば人の話をしっかり聴いているつもりでも、誤解したり曲解したり、都合よく解釈してしまったりすることは多々あるし、相手の音をしっかり聴いているつもりでも、音楽が交じり合わない場合は多い…それは何故か。

それは「それぞれが、互いに了解し合っている約束事に従って、やるべきことをちゃんとやっていたなら、互いのやることは自ずとかみ合うはず」といった思い込みが、この社会に蔓延しているからだ。学校の教室で、全員が教壇に向かい、「互いには向き合うことなく」授業受けていた、子供時代の形態そのままが、社会に反映されている。互いの意識は、「約束事」と「自分がやること」ばかりに向いており、瞬間瞬間に「互いに向かっては、開かれていない」。だから、本当の意味での合奏が成り立ちにくくなっている。もちろん僕は、音楽に限った話をしている訳ではない。

「きく」だの「みる」だのといった、「入り口器官」に関する言葉を使いながら、何かを「感じている」つもりにはならないことだ。全ての感覚は、そのずっと奥にある何かで「味わう」ことを通じて、開かれてゆく。それによって僕たちの日常的な感覚、互いのみえ方や互いの関係性は、きっと変わってくる。「きく」をこえた時、互いの声は今よりもずっと、きこえてくるはずだ。

テレシンカ・ペレイラ（米国・ブラジル）

アメリカ壁

メキシコとアメリカの
間を区切る境界線
壁は　巨大な　恥知らずの　牢獄
植民地からの貧困労働者が
アメリカ帝国に入ることは
遮断する
壁は存在し続けるだろう
国々の歴史の中で
けだものの警告の叫びとして
沈黙の　威嚇の通告として
でっち上げの「アメリカの夢」の
希望に燃え　やって来る移民たちへの
壁は　監史と囚人を共に
同じ監獄に縛る　芸術品だ
時代の後退を　促進する
封建地主の搾取　小作人の貧困へと
壁は増大して行くだろう
密輸　不法出入国　人間の奴隷化
壁の中にやがて埋められる
鋼鉄のアメリカの心臓
不法入国の　労働者の血の心臓
やがてひとつになるだろう
人間はいない　塔の中で
塔の下の　人間はいない
地平線に空はない　国で
二滴の涙は　すぐに乾く
ここは砂漠だ

………………

（水崎野里子和訳）

Teresinka Pereira (USA / BRAZIL)

THE U.S.A WALL

The border between Mexico
and the United States
is an enormous and shameless prison
both sides of the Wall.
The Wall is a barrier to stop
the peons from the colonies
from entering the U.S.A Empire.
The Wall will be present
in the history of the nations
as a beastly shout of warning,
a visible and silent frightening
message to the immigrants arriving
with aspirations to the fictional
“American Dream”.
The Wall is an artifact to bind
guards and prisoners in the same jail.
It promotes a regression of time
to feudal greed, and peasant poverty.
The Wall will increase smuggling,
traffic, and slavery of human beings.
Inside the Wall there will be buried
an American heart of steel
at the side of another heart
of the workers blood.
They will be united
in this no one’s tower,
in no one’s land under
a horizon without sky,
like two transient tears
in the desert.
....

草倉哲夫（日本・福岡）

翻訳『ハーバースパイの魔法の歌』*より（1）
訳詩集『ハーバースパイの魔法の歌』の出版にあたって

現代の地球がいろんな所で悲鳴をあげるニュースや、その実際を目の当たりにするにつけ、自分を形成している西欧の人間中心主義に一定の疑問を持つようになってきた。世界の存在は人間のために神が創ったのだという信仰に、キリスト教徒でなくても影響を受けている。

それに代る世界観を自分の中に発見するために、インドへも行ってみた。私たち日本人の根底には、仏教の教えがこれまた染み込んでいるのである。

日本人のものの視方を追求する想いは、さらに『万葉』『記紀』その先の縄文へと帰っていった。現代の縄文である、沖縄の『おもろそうし』、アイヌの『アイヌ神話集』に関心を持つのは当然であった。

そんな中、今の世界を支配する（キリスト教国家）アメリカへ二〇〇四年に半月の旅をした。消費文明の元祖、アメリカのウオール街は、今世紀初めにアルカイーダによって爆破されたツインタワービルのグランドゼロのすぐ隣にある。私は、自分の中に巣食っている消費文明と、それに反発するテロリストの心にもてあそばれながら、附近を逍遥していた。

こんなところに博物館があった。アメリカ独立当時のクラシックな建物に「ネイティヴアメリカン展」の垂れ幕が下がっていた。会場には、昔のインデアンの生活から、現代のネイティヴアメリカンの苦難の現状までが展示されていた。腕を組みじっと私を見つめる若者たちの等身大写真。または、草原の彼方を見上げるまなざし。彼等はこの巨大な消費文明の中で何を考えているのだろうか。

私は、彼らのアンソロジー（詩集）の小さな本を手にとった。何行か読んでいるうちに、不思議な感覚にとらわれた。それは縄文の世界に通じているようであった。考えてみれば、それは不思議なことではない。彼等は、東アジアの縄文人たちの末裔なのだから。

私は、さっそくその小さな本を買った。原題は、『ネイティヴアメリカンの歌と詩のアンソロジー』とあり、ブリアン・スワン編である。

帰国後、私は＜自分のために＞その本を全部訳してノートした。そ

Tetsuo Kusakura (Japan / Fukuoka)

From His Japanese Translation Book: *The Magical Song of the Harberspei*

Preface

Hearing the news reports, like the earth screams in places, or witnessing the reality for myself, I started to have a question on the humanism in the west, which was supposed to have formed myself. I am not a Christian, but I had come influenced by the faith that the world was created by the god for humans, us.
For discovering my own thoughts to be replaced, I traveled to India We, Japanese, have been also deeply influenced by Buddhism..
In the quest of Japanese own thoughts, I returned further, to *The Ten Thousand Leaves*: the collected poems in the early age of Japan, or *The Ancient Records of Japan,* then led into the Jomon period, in more far ancient times of Japan.. In the course, I took the interest in such books as *The Collection of Ancient Ryukyu Songs,* or *Ainu Mythology,* which will be natural.
In the course of the time, I traveled also to stay in U.S. for half a year, in 2004. The Wall Street, the center of the economic business in New York, is situated just next to the ground zero, the Twin tower building, the Al Qaida destroyed. I had been wandering in the neighborhood areas, swinging myself between the economic modern civilization and the terrorism against it. The civilization for the great consumption rooted deep inside me, too.
There, I discovered a historical museum. The building looked like a classical one, like in the style of the American Revolutionary War. It had a hanging cloth noted as The Native American Exhibition. In the halls they exhibited their information, from the life style of them in the old days, to their hardships they have to face at the present time. .There was a photo of the young people life-sized staring at me with their arms crossed. Or, they looked far, beyond the grass plain. What were they think in this great economic consumption age?

れがこの本である。だから私家版である。

二〇〇四年冬　　草倉哲夫

註

＊草倉哲夫訳『ハーバースパイの魔法の歌』(二〇一〇年、私家版)

I happened to pick up a small book of their anthology of poems. Reading lines, I had a strange feeling. It seemed linking with the Jomon world. It was not strange to think, because they were descendants of the Jomon people in the east Asia.
No sooner than I purchased the small book. The title was Native American Song-Poems: The Brian Swan edited version.
Returning to japan, I translated all the poems in the book, for me and noted them down. This is the book. It is my own made, for myself, not for sale.

In the winter, 2004. Tetsuo Kusakura.

* From *The Magical Songs of the Haberspei* (2010, Asakura Shorin, Fukuoka, Japan): TETSUO KUSAKURA the Japanese Editior & Japanese Translator. The book has another Preface, translated into Japanese, originally written by Brian Swann

翻訳：『ハーバースパイの魔法の歌：ネイティヴアメリカンの歌と詩のアンソロジー』より（1）

鹿の歌（ナバホ）

彼らは動き出した
私のほうへ
私の歌にいざなわれ
私は
いま
つややかな黒い鳥なのだ
黒い山の
道がはじまる頂から
やって来る
今　まっさかりの花々の間を通り
やって来る
今　　露の間をぬって
今
花粉を浴びて
やって来る
今
そこに
鹿が
おどろいて
廻りだした
雄が
左足から
雌が
右足から
動物たちが
私を
待っている

＊『ハーバースパイの魔法の歌：ネイティヴアメリカンの歌と詩のアンソロジー』（二〇一〇年、朝倉書林）より

Deer Song (NAVAJO)

they start
towards me
to my song
I am
now
a glossy blackbird
from Black Mountain
on top
where the trail starts
coming
now among flowers of all kinds
coming
now in among the dew
now
among the pollen
coming
now
right there
the deer
startled
turning
left foot first
the male
right first
the female
the quarry
they
want me

＊英語版はSONG of the SKY: VERSIONS OF NATIVE AMERICAN SONG-POEMS, P.29. (1993, The University of Massachusetts Press, USA): REVISED AND EXPANDED EDITION BRIAN SWANN/ FORWOD BY BARRY O'CONNELL

新谷頼子（日本・大阪）
Yoriko Shintani (Japan / Osaka)

俳句連作：
カール・バルトと共に

Haiku Sequence:
With Karl Barth

元旦や
バイオリンひき
聖日課

New Year's decision;
to play Mozart
Music with violin
and read the chapter
of the Bible every day
(Brevier)

秋晴れに
バルト家の人々と
日本庭園

Fine autumn day,
Markus, Rose Marie Barth
and I walk in a
Japanese garden
in Osaka

女児服を
バーゼルから
贈られ
初節句
（娘はるか誕生
　昭和51年9月13日）

Baby clothes
from Basel
in Switzerland
Celebrated
new seasonal
girl's festival

復活祭
十字架上のキリスト像
老書斎

On Easter day
in front of the wall
of CRUCIFIXION
the old scholar
of his library

満月に
バルドの名を

On the full moon
night

頂き
娘誕生

a new-born baby-
girl HARUKA
named after Barth.

五月雨
反ナチ闘争より
生まれし
バルメン宣言

In my breeze
Karl BARTH
with Barmen
Declaration
in his hands
have Anti-Nazis-Strife

晩秋や
繰り返し読む
教会教義学

Late Autumn
again and again
I try to read
DIE KIRCHLICHE
DOGMATIK
(the Gospel of the Bible)

寂光の
バルト家の
墓地
緑の光
（寂・静かな日光
　　　がさす　うす光り）

In the twilight
the graveyard
of the Barth in Basel
the beautiful green
forest

クリスマスの朝
しょうがクッキー焼く
ロマ書読む

On the Christmas Morning
Baking Christ
Mas ginger
Cookies,
the Epistle to
the Romans
I read.

梅は実に
神が人となる

Oh God's Grace!
happenings

恵の出来事
天使舞ゆ

plum blossoming,
like dancing
Angels
brings fruit;
it is
So unto me god's
Grace.

(English Translated by the Author)

編集者註：カール・バルト（1886-1968）はスイス・バーゼル生まれのキリスト教神学者。日本訪問の際に筆者が大阪を案内。バルトは彼女の俳句を賞賛した。

Editor's Note: Karl Barth(1886-1968) is a Christian theologian, who was born in Basel of Switzerland. When he visited Japan, in Osaka, Yoriko the author of these haiku poems, showed him around in Osaka. He admired her haiku poems.

メンターム

市川つた（日本・茨城）
Tsuta Ichikawa (Japan / Ibaraki)

老いはポジティブに
Let It Be Positive：The Old Age

老いは誰にでもやってくる自然現象
逃げ切れた人はいない
老いを捉えた人　老いに囚われた人は幸せだ
経験したということ生きたということ
老いを追って書き留めたいと思う

Everyone grows old in a natural phenomenon
That no one can escape from
These ones are happy who have grasped it or
Who have been captured by it
Having experienced it means we lived life
I want to note it down in a search for the old age

老いをどのように受け　どのように凝視め
どのように記録し語り
やさしく糖衣錠にして飲み込むか
どう生きたら充実して生きられるか
後悔せず慨嘆もせず
ありのままを受け入れ微笑し

How we should welcome or watch it
How we should we record and tell it
How we should turn it into a sugar-coated pill
to take more easily I wonder
How we should have a satisfactory life
Not regretting nor lamenting over
Receiving things as they are: smiling

老いと肩組んで歩調をあわせ
もう少し先まであの曲がり角まで
汀までと足を伸ばす
ゆとりと励ましの一歩が
ゆるり老いの手を引いてくれる

Shoulder to shoulder keeping paces with it
We can walk a bit far to the corner
Then to the beach we take steps farther
The one step relaxing and encouraging
Will pull our old hands leisurely

さよならはゆっくりでいい
懐かしさを歩み返して微笑もう
反芻して若さの中に帰る
老いはポジティブに歩むもの
住みぬけた地を　旅した地を
懐かしんで訪れる

Let us have slow farewells in no haste
Let us smile trailing back dear memories
Let us return to our youth ruminating them
We should walk the way of the old age positively
On the places we once lived or we travelled to
Let us have the visitations again in nostalgia

老いは遡りの楽しみを持つ
記憶の旅　追憶の旅を楽しむ
ゆっくりと歩こう

It has the joy of trailing back
Let us enjoy again our travels
In our memory or in the nostalgia
Let us walk with slow steps

(Translator: Noriko Mizusaki)

酒井力（日本・佐久）

弓道詩編：意識の底の静寂に

男は弓を押し開き
「会（かい）」*に入っている

静寂は
足もとから
音もなく溢れ出し

やがて雄大な川となって
滔々と流れていく

水の流れ込む意識の先は
確かに「死」という
ひとつの瞬間に違いない

男は「会」によって自己と出会い
気息を丹田に充溢し
生命エネルギーを
一気に発散

自己という宇宙のビッグバン
さながら——

矢を放つ「離れ」は
即「残心（身）」
それまでの「良否」を決する
自己の姿となる

原注＊「会」とは弓道の｛射法八節｝——「足踏み」「胴造り」「弓構え」「打ち起こし」
「会」「離れ」「残心」の終末部分の最も重要な一つの段階をいう

Tsutomu Sakai (Japan / Saku)

In the Quietness
——On the Japanese Archery: from the Series

An archer pushed out his bow
Into the stage of Full Draw (Kai)*

Quietness up
From at his feet
Overflows in silence

Gathering into a grand river
It goes flow fluent

The water will go into the end
In the spirit is to be indeed
An instant called death

He meets himself in the stage of Full Draw (Kai)
Gathering up the air-breaths in full in the abdomen
Then he releases
All of his life energy at once

The big bang in the cosmos: he is the one
As if——

The stage of Release (Hanare): Releasing an arrow
Then just to the next stage of Remaining Spirit (Zanshin)
He has to determine himself how good or bad his posture was
In the previous stage

The Author's Note=Full Draw (Kai) is one of the most important stage in the final part. In the EIGHT STAGES OF SHOOTING FOR THE JAPANESE ARCHERY: Footing (Ashibumi), Forming the Torso (Dozukuri), Readying the Bow (Yugamae), Raising the Bow (Uchiokoshi), Full Draw (Kai), Release (Hanare), Remaining Spirit (Zanshin).

(Translator: Noriko Mizusaki)

初鶯

駅の裏手の駐車場に車を止めて
歩いていると
山間から人知れずやってきた
影のようなものが
不意に
耳の奥をくすぐるように
たった一度
頭上で鳴いた

はじめはすべるように
やわらかく
細く艶っぽい一瞬の閃光は
爽やかな静寂を
いまも心のなかにとどめたままだ

桜花の季節
初鶯は右耳で聴くと縁起がよい
と中国の故事にもあるというが……

（街角を曲がればそれは旅である）
と言って時代から消えた
数学者の足跡を追って
鶯は鳴いていたのかも知れない

世間という世俗にまみれた書物とは別に
太古からいのちをつないできているであろう
小さな影を
呼び寄せるつもりか

駅のプラットフォームのスピーカーから
「ホーッ　ホケキョ」と
単調で無遠慮な
人工音が響いている

The First Singing of a Bush Warbler

Having parked my car in the parking lot
Behind a station
I was walking when suddenly I heard
Some bird tiny sang out only one time
High above me just like it tickled
The deepest part of my mind ears
As if it had come over there
From among mountains far
Not with any notices by the people
It was a shadow: to me

At first the cry was soft like sliding
As the instant flush thin and full of charms
It has left a kind of fresh quietness
Still staying till now in my mind depths

In the season of cherry blossoms
The first singing of bush warblers gives you luck
When you hear it in your right ear
That a Chinese old record noted down: they say… Yet

(Turning at the corner will lead you to a travel)
Some mathematician preaching so stepped out of his age
Following his footsteps might have they been crying

Indifferent to the worldly books all covered with dusts
Since the ancient times having linked down wild life
The tiny figure in nature
They are calling to come?

Out of the speaker in the platform of the station
The artificial warbling I hear coming resound
Monotonous and unreserved
Mimicking them

(Translator: Noriko Mizusaki)

岡耕秋（日本・長崎・諫早）

Yasuaki Oka (Japan / Nagasaki / Isahaya)

回遊庭園

My Round-Trip Garden

むかし　山麓の尾根にまたがり
有明海や雲仙を展望する
標高二五メートル
高低差五メートルの傾斜地に立つ
古いルーテル教会を譲り受けた時
ここに終の棲家を建てたいと思った

Decades ago when I happened to be gifted with
An old Lutheran Church
I thought I would like to build my last house there:
It was standing up across the foothill ridges
Built on a slanting slope with five meters difference
From the lowest to the top spot
It was twenty five meters up above the sea level
Showing a wonderful panorama of the Ariake Sea
and Mt. Unzen

家を建てて
そのぐるりに分断されてきた
四つの高低差のある庭を四つの階段でつないだ
そうして二十年近く経ち
いつのまにか
ちいさな回遊庭園ができあがった

I had my house built and
Linked the four small gardens with the four stairs
The four gardens had four differences in the rolling
Each of them had been divided from each other

Surrounding the house: with no links having had before
Over twenty years passed since then
Sometime and somehow
A kind of the small round-trip garden has been made up

今は四階建ての町役場が立つ一画には
むかしそのひとの生家があった
屋敷を囲む広い庭の
多様な植物の中で育った
そのひとが嫁いできて
なによりも願っていたのは豊かな緑の庭

In a block where now a four-storied town hall stands
Once there stood a house where my wife was born
She grew up there surrounded with so many species of plants
They were planted up all in a garden around her large house
Then she married me and what she wished me first of all was
A green garden rich in trees and flowers before anything

門扉のある南西の庭には
シュガーメープルにイロハモミジ
泰山木ともっこうばら　海棠に沈丁花
ライラックとダグウッド
生垣に珊瑚樹　ばらの花壇
下草にはビンカ・ミノールとムスカリ

In the southwest garden where the gate door stands
A Sugar Maple and a Japanese Maple
Two trees of Southern Magnolia and Banksia Roses
A Flowering Crab Apple and two shrubs of Daphne
Lilacs and Dogwoods you can see
For the hedge grows a bush of Coral Formation
Flower beds of roses: there
For the undergrowth: Vinca Minors and Grape Hyacinths

南東の庭には
高くなりすぎて梢を落とされたモミの木
百日紅(さるすべり)や乙女椿　金木犀　カラタネオガタマ
枇杷やすもも　金柑
私のばら苑とそのひとの自然園
この季節は矢車草の群落

In the southeast garden
A Fir tree stands whose tree tops were clipped
Because they had grown up too tall
Four plants of Crape Myrtle and two of Otome Camellia
A Fragrant Olive tree and a Banana shrub
The Loquat and the Japanese Plum
A Kumquat: you see
My rose garden and her natural garden
In this season Cornflowers are out in clusters

一段低い北東の庭には
モミジバフウの大木と棕櫚
ハクモクレン　オガタマノキ
何種類かの紫陽花　桜桃とブルーベリー
クレマチスやさまざまな鉢
ちっぽけな池とメダカの分校

In the northeast garden by one stair lower
Two big tree of Redgum and a Hemp Palm
A White Magnolia and a Michelia tree
Several species of Hydrangea in the bush
Cherries and Blueberries for fruit
Various kinds of potted plants; like Clematis
In a tiny pond you see
A small group of Japanese Rice Fish

北西の狭い庭には
その落葉のせいでご近所に疎まれて

低く伐られた樫のマッシュルーム
月桂樹に
シャリンバイにひいらぎ南天
つつじや沈丁花

In the northwest small garden
Mushrooms of an Oak: the tree was cut shorter
Because neighbors complained of the fallen leaves so thick
A Laurel tree
Several plants of Indian Hawthorns and Japanese Mahonias
Azaleas and Daphnes will bloom in full: you see

友人や知人たちが寄せた樹木や花々には
いくつもの思い出
ちいさな回遊庭園は植物の見出しでつづられる大きな物語
階段の手すりを伝って
老いたそのひとが庭を歩いている

These trees and flowers
My friends and friendly people gifted to me
Have dear memories for myself
My small round-trip garden is a big story for me
Spelled with the indexes of my plants
My wife who has got elderly now is walking in our garden
Supported and led on the handrails of our stairs

(Translator: Noriko Mizusaki)

家を建てる
Building A House

家にはハウスガイスト*が棲むという
年数をかけて何枚も設計図を書いて
いろいろ考えあぐねて
それなりに住みよい家を作ったが
ハウスガイストを呼び寄せることは
すっかり忘れていた

They say in our houses dwell the house spirits
I built my house at last
I think it pretty good one for us to dwell in:
I had drawn so many plans taking years
Thinking on so many ideas
Though I did completely forget inviting house spirits
To the house

その時から
なにかを失ってしまったような気がする
あたらしい木の香りや真白い壁に遮られて
書きかけの小説の筆が進まなくなった
ふっとやってくる詩想が
すぐに姿を消してしまう

Since I got aware of it
I feel like I have lost something precious
Shuttered with the fresh wood fragrance or white walls
My pen writing a novel is sometimes stopped unfinished
Even when the idea of my poem happens to occur to me
Soon it will vanish away

昔　胸の底に潜んでいて
わたしのものがたり書いてと

いつもささやいていた
ニンフがどこかに姿を消してしまった
明るい照明や
部屋をながれる透明な外気に怯えて

Many years before
A nymph having lurked at the bottom of my mind
She whispered always to me to write her story
She was gone somewhere
Frightened of the illumination too bright or
The transparent open air coming to invade into my room

家にはハウスガイストが
棲めるような
秘密の空間がいるのだ
そこでは時間が凝縮して澱んでいて
思い出や面影や昔の囁きや声までが
とじこめられるような

Our houses need secret spaces
Where the house spirit can dwell
There time keeps condensed and stagnant
Memories and dear ones' old images
Old whispers and even old voices will stay
Trapped

(Translator: Noriko Mizusaki)

訳者註：

＊ハウスガイスト＝元はドイツ語。HAUSGEIST. GEISTは日本語では精神、霊、心の意。英語ではGHOST（幽霊）、GUEST（招客）に似る（ドイツ語では客はGAST）が、詩中にニンフ（妖精と訳す）とあるのでハウススピリット（＝家霊）と訳した。幽霊・招客と解しても構わないと思う。原作の岡先生の説明ではドイツだけではなくヨーロッパ中に拡がるオカルト伝承であるとのこと。ちなみに、特に日本の地方地域ではいまだに台所や居間に神棚があり日頃拝している。

すなわち家に棲む保護霊や先祖の霊に日頃拝礼する。また地鎮祭と称して新しく家を建てる前に神主を呼んで土地の邪霊（悪鬼）を鎮めてもらう式（神道）もある。

2019年度パンドラ賞発表
佐々木洋一さん

感謝状

佐々木洋一様

宮城県から長年発信の、継続・一貫する、やさしい日本語のリズムで語りかけるようなあなたの詩作に感謝し、ここに賞状を授与します。あなたは日本の新体詩に日本語のやさしさと抒情性を持続させました。

令和一年六月二十四日

世界詩人会議大阪大会記念

日本会長水崎野里子

松浦恭子（日本・京都）

自然と共に

晴れた日　気分は明るく　楽しい
曇りの日　心も曇る
雨の日　気分は湿っぽい
私は思う　あぁ！　私は自然と共にあると
自然から　到底逃れることは出来ないと
周りにある自然の声に傾聴し、平安と安らぎを得よう

Yasuko Matsuura (Japan / Kyoto)

Along with nature

On a fine day, my feeling is bright and I am filled with joy,
When it's cloudy, I have clouds somewhere in my mind.
On a rainy day, I am in the dumps, and I notice that we are living with nature and I'll never escape from nature.
Listen to the voices of nature around us, and we may get a peace and ease.

(Poem and the translation by Yasuko Matsuura)

三沢晏子（日本・東京）

Yasuko Misawa (Japan / Tokyo)

書簡と絵葉書

前略

旅の中でたまに話しすれちがい笑をかわした
ローマ大学での数行の詩を見せて頂いて優しい人だと、
入手したばかりの詩集何回も何回も——
昨日もジャカランダ見に一緒でした。
あなたの心臓の鼓動に觸れたくて、
あなたの心の叫びを聴きたいと——何回も、
でも詩っていゝなあ　こんなに自由にものが云えて、
俳句みたいに削ってけずって何かをくっつけて、じゃなく
口から出たあなたの言葉が詩になってころがってくる
どうやらあなたが蒔いた花に魅了されちゃったみたい。
毎日ぶらんといる私の心をそんなことしていていいの！とゆさぶられた気持ちです。
大切な本をありがとうございました。心の糧と致します、お約束なので愚作ですが絵葉書送らせて頂きます。この一枚がなかなか見当たらず大変遅れましたことお侘び致します。又いつかお会い出来たら嬉しく存じます。
お健やかに、お過ごしくださいませ。
六月七日　　三沢晏子拝
水崎野里子様

三沢晏子・絵葉書

毎日ぶらんと過している私の心をそんなことしてていいの！とゆすぶられた気持ちです
大切な本をありがとうございました。心の糧と致します。
お約束なので駄作ですが絵葉書送らせて頂きます
この一枚がなかなか見当らず大変遅れましたこと
お詫び致します　又いつかお会い出来たら嬉しく
存じます。
お健やかに！お過しくださいませ
六月七日　三沢晏子拝
水崎野里子様

佐々木洋一（日本・宮城）

ねんぶらん

ゆりかごゆれて
ねんぶらん
ゆれて　ゆられて
めざめよ　こども
いのちのじかん
たれにもじゃまされず
めざめよ　こども
このよのめざめ

ゆりかごゆれて
ねんぶらん
ゆれて　ゆられて
ねんぶらん　ねんぶらん
ゆれろよ　こども
こころのじかん
たれにもじゃまされず
ゆれろよ　こども
はだしのしゅんかん

ゆりかごゆれて
ねんぶらん
ゆれて　ゆられて
ねんぶらん　ねんぶらん
ねむれよ　こども
ねむりのじかん
たれにもじゃまされず
ねむれよ　こども
やみよのねむり

Yoichi Sasaki (Japan / Miyagi)

Goody-Baby-Sleepy

Swinging is your cradle
Goody-Baby-Sleepy
Swinging / Swung
Goody-Baby-Sleepy Goody
Wake up you a baby
In a time of your life
Nobody can disturb you
Wake up you a baby
Awaken to this world

Swinging is your cradle
Goody-Baby-Sleepy
Swinging / Swung
Goody-Baby-Sleepy Goody
Swing you a baby
Now the time of your heart
Nobody can disturb you
Swing you the baby
While you naked- footed

Swinging is your cradle
Goody-Baby-Sleepy
Swinging / Swung
Goody-Baby-Sleepy Goody
Sleep well you the baby
It is a time of your sleeping
Nobody can disturb you
Have you the time
Sleeping for dark nights

(Translator: Noriko Mizusaki)

ユー・ハンキュー（韓国・ソウル）

故郷の家

あたらしくできた道を
とぼとぼと

懐かしさが
風船のように膨らみ

村の入り口から
井戸を過ぎ
酒蔵を過ぎて
同級生たちの家を通り過ぎるまで

胸は高鳴って

客間の縁側に
ランプの火が
つり下がったまま

居間に
灯油壺のともしびと
その影

うちのじいちゃん
書を読む声
朗々たり！

（日本語訳：秋葉信雄）

Yoo Hankyu (Korea / Seoul)

House of My Home Village

The road newly born
Plodding along

My happy memories
Swelling like a balloon

From the entrance to my village
Through the well
Through the brewer
Till passing through classmates' homes

My heart giving me a throb

At a drawing room's veranda
Fire of a lamp
Hanging down

At a living room
Low flame of the oil pot
And the shadow

My grandpa
Voice of reading out the writings
What a fruity voice!

(English Translated by Nobuo Akiba)

고향집

신작로
타박타박

그리움
풍선 되어

동네 어귀
우물가 지나
술도가 지나
한교네 집 지나도록

가슴은 뛰고

사랑마루
남폿불
걸어놓고

사랑방
호롱불
그림자

우리 할배
글 읽는 소리
낭랑타~!

(ユーさん原文韓国語詩)

山本由美子（日本・姫路）

沈黙

言われたように
一度読んだら
手紙は捨てます

つかの間の煌きが
褪せぬよう

罵りでも蔑みでもいい
言葉をください

沈黙は死より孤独

Yumiko Yamamoto (Japan / Himeji)

Silence

As you requested,
I will dispose of your letter
After reading it once,

So that I can keep
The briefest impression.

Tell me anything
Even if it is abuse or contempt.

Silence makes me feel more lonely
Than death.

(Translated by the Author)

透明のかけら

はらはらと
記憶の破片が
落ちてくる
私の辺りを
埋めつくす
ひとつひとつを
拾い集めて
空にむかって
放ちましょう
透明のかけらに
変わるよう
穏やかに
優しく
愛しさをこめて

ぱらぱらと
言葉の響きが
降ってくる
私の周りで
重なり合う
ひとえひとえに
息を吹きかけ
空気の中に
浮かべましょう
溶けて永遠に
届くまで
こわれないよう
軽やかに
心をつくして

Transparent Pieces

Pieces of memory
Are drifting down.
They are surrounding me.
I will release them
One by one
Toward the sky
Mildly,
Softly
And heartily
So that they can change
Into transparent pieces.

The echoes of words
Are falling down.
They are piling up around me.
I will blow on words
One by one
Into the air
Lightly,
Merrily
And sincerely
So that they can get
To eternity.

(Translated by the Author)

中尾彰秀（日本・和歌山）

「序」五行聖地[*1]

一、生命の中心は○と∞等しく——地
二、地球は聖なるTAOやかな星———水
三、医食同源と「呼吸のソムリエ」——火
四、森羅万象の内なる光、古代現在未來貫いて——風
五、何もなくて何でもあるここ永遠の永遠——空（クウ）

聖地とは地球であり森羅万象たる自分自身。

*1. 五行聖地　2018年5月、森羅通信の会

Akihide Nakao (Japan / Wakayama)

Preface of *The Holy places for Five Elements*[*2]

1. In the center of Life, zero equals to eternity——Ground
2. The earth planet is a holy and GRACEful star——Water
3. Healing and foods in the same source and the Sommelier of breaths——Fire
4. The inner light of all things, all times through the ancient, the present and the future——Wind
5. There exist nothing yet everything in the cosmos: on this point be eternity of eternity——Air

A holy place is the earth planet itself and yourself: one of all the things in the cosmos.

*2= The English Title of Author's Poetry Book Published in Japanese (2018, Shinrabansho-no Kai).

(Translator: Noriko Mizusaki)

今ここに花

あるない狭間の波動を一点に凝縮し
今ここにある理由が今ここにない理由を
ほんの少し上回って今ここに花を咲かせる
理由とは不可思議の総量（バランス）
この世とあの世同時に束ねた空（クウ）よ

Now Here A Flower Is

Be and Not Be: the waving motions condense into one
The reason why it here is a bit upper than it not here
Into it here blooms out: a flower opened and came out
The reason is a gross mass of the mysterious balances
It is in the eternity our binding this world and the next

(Translator: Noriko Mizusaki)

中尾彰秀撮影
A Photo by Akihide Nakao

山口敦子（日本・東京）
Atsuko Yamaguchi (Japan / Tokyo)

山頭火絶唱
A Song of Santoka: My Dear Poet

一

幼い　我が児（こ）を　残して消えた
母の　辛さを　噛みしめて
青葉　若葉の　燃ゆる日に
これから歩む　人生を
誰に　託して　良いものか
一人　涙に　暮れる日よ

Leaving a child behind she vanished
Thinking of her hardship again today
Green leaves and young leaves bright
Who should I trust my life to: I wonder
I drop tears alone thinking my mother

二

学びの校舎を　くぐってみたが
瞼　離れぬ　母の顔
若さ　強さを　望んでも
心は　空（うつろ）　宙（ちゅう）に舞う
話す　相手は　何処にか
旅に　求めて　今日も行く

Through the gate of my school I studied
But my mother’s image haunted me
Even if I wish myself youth and strength

My mind empty in the air flutters around
Where is my dear or mates I can talk with?
I go travel also today seeking for the ones

三

あてのないまま　流離うちに
神や　仏の　情あり
辿りながらの　俳句の旅人
自由に詠う　生涯ならば
生きて行けよう　私でも
母よ　見てくれ　いつまでも

With no destinations for my traveling
Gods and Buddha gave mercy I found
I a traveler making haiku on the way
If it my mission: a free poet for my life
I could live through even if I lonesome
Mother! Watch me! Forever what I am

「母上様……」
Oh! Mother! In the heaven…

唄：佐々木宏
Singer: Hiroshi Sasaki

(Translator: Noriko Mizusaki)

エドワード・レビンソン（日本・千葉・米国）

前記日本語版：『ぼくの植え方』（岩波書店刊より）

spring buds…
clenched fists waiting
to break open

春の芽や閉じて 待つ拳こじ開けよ

　ぼくらの家で行った「オープン・ガーデン・デー」に人々が来訪し、一番近い鉄道の駅から歩いて来たと言う人がいた。ぼくは今まで一度も歩いたことはなく、四〇分かかったと言うので驚いた。地方に住む者にとって最低の必需品は、車か少なくとも軽トラックである。今ぼくにはその両方がある。古い軽のダンプトラックは、道路工事用の砂利や、薪ストーブのための木や、庭用の土や、生活のための水や、趣味のサーフ・ボードを運ぶ。お下がりのシトロエン（ぼくと同じ「外人だ」）は、やっとのことで狭くて急な道を走ることが出来、常に泥まみれだ。この車は人々やカメラや作品を運ぶのに都合がよい。
　エコライフをすることには幾つかの矛盾がある。どこへでも徒歩や自転車で行けば、よりエコロジカルで健康的だろう。だが純粋主義者でないものにとっては、車は生活を楽にする。車にエネルギーを使う分、ぼくは自分のエネルギーを蓄え、その他のこと、例えば写真撮影や著作、草刈りや植樹、あるいは夏のサーフィンのために使う。

（日本語文：エドワード・レビンソン）

Edward Levinson (Japan / Chiba / USA)

From *Whisper of the Land:*
Excerpt from chapter: “Never a Free Ride”

spring buds…
clenched fists waiting
to break open

春の芽や 閉じて 待つ拳こじ開けよ
haru no meya, tojite matsu kobushi, kojiake yo

*****

On one of our Open Garden days, someone showed up at Solo Hill out of breath and sweaty, saying she had walked from the closest train station. I had never done the three kilometers on foot and was surprised to hear it had taken forty minutes. For most people living in the countryside, having a car or at least a small truck is a necessity.

I have both. My beat-up old mini dump truck carries gravel for the road, wood for the stove, dirt for the garden, water for life, and my surfboard for fun. The car, a hand-me-down French Citroen (a foreigner like me), barely makes it up the steep, narrow road to our house, and always seems to be covered with mud. It carries people, cameras, and artwork.

Living an eco life requires compromises. While it may be more ecological and healthier to walk or bicycle everywhere, unless you are a purist, a car helps make life easier. When I drive, I am saving my energy and my time for something else like photography, writing, cutting the grass, planting trees, or some seasonal surfing.

水崎野里子　Noriko Mizusaki

The Essay Note on Edward's Photo & His Works
エッセイ：エドワードさんの写真と俳文について

The Original English Version by the Author
English Checks by Edward Levinson: 通称Edo＝恵道

解説：水崎野里子
英語チェック：エドワード・レビンソン

When I first read Edward Levinson's *WHISPER OF THE LAND: VISIONS OF JAPAN*, (Fine Line Press, 2014), I was struck by some kind of strange feeling of nostalgia. I found and recognized in the book many things, people, and natural landscapes, which those of us living in Tokyo have long lost, thrown away, or forgotten in the name of modernity. Edward, who was born and grew up in US, showed us the feelings he found in native Japanese landscapes. I am very grateful and happy to see them.

私が初めてエドワード・レビンソン氏の著『日本の囁き』(邦名、2014年、ニュージーランドで刊行）を読んだ時、一種の郷愁のような不思議な感動に襲われた。ご本の中には、東京ではとうの昔に失われたか放棄された、あるいは近代の名の下で忘れられてしまったモノたち、人々、自然の風景、それらがあった！見つけた！エドさんはアメリカで生まれ育ったのであるが、氏が日本の土着の風景の中に見出した喜怒哀楽を私たちに示してくださった。私にはそれは郷愁、ノスタルジアと映じた。嬉しかった。ありがとうと感謝申し上げる。

The modernization movement beginning with the Meiji Reformation was based fundamentally on imitating the Western countries. In Japanese, we also called them the Western Powers (=西欧列強)：UK, USA, France, Germany, Russia and Italy. This "imitating" was repeated once again after Japan's defeat at the end of the World War II and continues today. It might have provided some internationalization or globalization to Japan, especially in the name of industrialization and the development of the IT technology. But at the same time, some things which were once peculiar to Japan, started to vanish or be rejected, just because they had become “old” or “oriental”, and not “international.” I wonder if we have been living in a “lost country”? Why don’t we as individuals speak out more?

明治時代の「文明開化」によって始められた日本の近代化運動は基本的には、日本人が当時西欧列強と呼んだ国々——当時はイギリス、アメリカ合州国、フランス、ドイツ、ロシア、イタリアなど——の模倣に基盤を置いていた。さらにその西欧大国模倣は終戦と呼ばれる第二次世界大戦の敗北以降に再び繰り返された。それは工業化と情報工学発展の名目の下では、日本にいささかの国際化、あるいはグローバリゼイションをもたらしたかもしれない。だが同時に、かつては日本に固有であったモノたちは、単に「古くなった」か「東洋的で」、「国際的ではない」という理由で、消え去るか廃棄されて行った。私たちは「失われた国」に住んでいたのか？どうして個人としてもっと意見を言わないのか？

The photo by Edward, an old woman walking, carrying a huge bamboo basket on her back, dressed in the *monpe* style, has been continuously haunting me since I first saw it a few years ago. Perhaps it is just my own personal nostalgia. Around twenty years ago, I also had watched a Nepalese woman carrying a huge bamboo basket on her back. At the time, we were just travelers trekking in some part of the Himalayan mountain area. She was sturdy and had quick steps, soon leaving us behind. Thank you Edward! So nostalgic! So Asiatic! I too like to wear *monpe* pants! You taught us this is a Japan we shouldn’t forget!

エドワードさんが撮影した、モンペ姿で背中に大きな竹籠を背負って歩くオバサンの写真。この写真は初めて見た時から長らく私を魅了して離れなかった。あるいはその理由は、私の個人的な郷愁だったのだろう。二十年程前、私はインドかネパールの女性が大きな竹籠を背負った姿を見た。当時、私たちはヒマラヤ地域でトレッキングをしていた単なる旅人であった。彼女は頑強で足取りは速く、すぐ私たちを置き去りにしてスタスタと大股で行ってしまった。エドさん、ありがとう！なつかしいです！アジア的です！私もモンペを穿きたいです！あなたは教えてくれました、「これが日本です！」と。

Lastly, I would like to say thanks to the US poets, especially to the poets of the Beat Generation and their followers, who once made brave protests and criticisms against US civilization and participated in anti-war activities. At the same time they appreciated (and recommended to us) a return to nature and the simple life. Gary Snyder in his poem of “Kyoto: March” and Jack Kerouac in his haiku on sparrows are two examples. Gary Snider had vegetables growing in the yard of his house in a suburb of Kyoto. Most of the outstanding poets of that generation came over to Japan and lived or stayed in Kyoto. Some traveled from Kyoto to India and other places. They loved and studied Zen philosophies, or Japanese culture, instead of worshipping success driven urban lives and Western civilization.

最後になるが、アメリカの詩人たち、特にビート世代の詩人たちと彼らの後継者に御礼を述べたい。彼等はかつて勇敢にアメリカの文明を批判して告発した。そして反戦運動に参加した。彼等は同時に自然に帰れと主張して質素な生活を推奨した。ゲイリー・スナイダーの詩「京都・三月」とジャック・ケラワックのスズメの俳句は代表的なその例である。スナイダーは京都郊外の自宅で野菜を栽培した。今、ビート世代の有名な詩人の多くは日本に渡来して京都に滞在、あるいは住んだ。何人かは京都からインドなど海外諸国へ旅立った。彼等は禅宗や日本文化を好み、学び、都市生活と西欧文明崇拝に人生の成功を求める価値観に反抗した。

メンターム

佐藤文夫（日本・千葉）

息を吹きかえす言葉たち

これまでほとんど使われなかった言葉が
近年になってよく使われるようになった
いわく隠蔽（いんぺい）　改竄（かいざん）　捏造（ねつぞう）　廃棄（はいき）　忖度（そんたく）
昨日や今日のテレビや新聞雑誌などで
お目にかからぬ日はなくなった

こんな言葉たちが生まれたその発信源は
アベ政権の　アベノミクスからであった
だが　かつてはこんな言葉たちがあった
一攫（いっかく）千金　丁か半か　一か八か　魔が差した
あぶく銭　上前（うわまえ）をはねる　濡れ手で粟（あわ）
元も子も失う　おけらになった　成れの果て
いかさま　八百長　ご法度（はっと）　尾羽（おは）うち枯らす
二進（にっち）も三進（さっち）もいかなくなった　一家心中する
これらの言葉の発信源は賭博からであった

いまこれらの賭博用語が　カジノとともに
またもや賑々（にぎにぎ）しく再現されようとしている

Fumio Sato (Japan / Chiba)

The Words Revive

The phrases which had been rarely used
These days I see and hear often used : for example
Inpei (Hiding): Kaizan (Falsification): Netsuzo (Forgery):
Haiki (Disposal): Sontaku (Consideration):
In the news media like T.V. and newspapers or in the journals
They originated in the Abenomics the Abe administration issued
While once we had such words and phrases:
Ikkaku Senkin (Taking One Bowl of Money at One Chance)
Cho ka Han ka (Odd or Even; in the number of the dice
= You Dare to Gamble):
Ichi ka Bati ka(=the same with Cho ka Han ka):
Maga Sashi ta (The magic came to deceive me):
Abukuzeni (Much money happened to come on you);
Uwamae wo Haneru (Brokers Take Much Money):
Nurete de Awa (Easy Too Many Gains):
Moto mo Ko mo Ushinau (Lost All the Money by Gambling):
Okera ni Natta (Became Penniless);
Nareno Hate (Became Penniless in the End):
Ikasama (Trickery Gambling):
Yaocho (Fraud: Fixed Game in Advance):
Gohatto (Taboos):
Oba Uchi Karasu (To be Down and Out: Became Penniless):
Nicchi mo Sacchi mo Ikanakunatta (You Stuck at the Dead End):
Ikka Shinjyu Suru (Committing All the Family Suicide Becoming
Penniless in Gambling):
These ones all originated in the gamble games
Now these terms are going to revive with fanfares
Together with the Casino

(Translator: Noriko Mizusaki)

佐藤文夫：エッセイ
「Doin'」から「天文台」へ――詩とジャズと――

私は1962年の春頃から、1976年の冬頃にかけて、「Doin'」(1962年～1965年)、「天文台」(1974年～1976年)という、ともに「詩とジャズ」の結合を標榜する、詩のグループに在籍していた。

このグループの存在は前後するが、ともに会則も月々の会費もなく、まったく出入りも自由、ただ毎月行われる「詩とジャズの会」に参加し、季刊で出される同人誌？に出稿するというものであった。月々の例会は、新宿のニュージャズ・ホール、明大前のキッド・アイラック・ホール(信濃デッサン館・無言館の窪島誠一郎氏経営)、渋谷のプルチネラ、池袋・パルコなどで定期的に行われた。この会の圧巻は、72年3月渋谷の西武デパートの駐車場で、聴衆を800名も集めて行われたイベントであった。この会には、詩人側から秋村宏、赤木三郎、佐藤文夫、白石かずこ、渋沢孝輔、諏訪優、富岡多恵子、中上哲夫、三好豊一郎、村田正夫、八木忠栄、吉増剛造などで、ニュージャズの側からは、沖至四重奏団、今田勝、藤川義明のNMEなどであった。それはジャズのミュージシャンたちの演奏と、私たち詩人の詩朗読とが出合う、いわば歌垣の会であった。

今、振り返ってみて凄いと思うことは、「Doin'」とその後の「天文台」に集まったさまざまな詩人たちが、ジャズのミュージシャンとともに、詩の朗読を行うという一点で、実際にこの会を、十数年も連続させ、持続させてきたということである。私たちは、初めから立派なマニフェストを掲げて出発した詩のグループではなかったが、今こうして振り返ってみると、ああこれが詩運動というものだったのか、と納得できることが多い。

ここで、先程の「Doin'」と「天文台」での、十数年にわたる詩とジャズの会の成果と反省点について、再考してみよう。

1972年の12月に、吉祥寺の「OZ」というライブハウスで、ニュージャズの沖至四重奏団との朗読会場でのことだった。聴衆は180人、50人は会場に入れず帰って頂いたこともあって、熱気と緊張感に満ちて会は進行していった。そのとき突然、ドラムのジョー水城が立ち上がり、マイクをつかむと「学芸会じゃないんだぞ！詩人たちもその気になってぶつけ合おうぜ！」と、緊急発言。とたんに会はピリリと一転。

Fumio Sato: Essay

On "Poetry at New Jazz": In Tokyo, Japan, ——from The Doin' to The Astronomical Observatory

From the spring in 1962 to the winter in 1976, I had been joining the two poetry groups, The Doin' (1962~1965) and The Astronomical Observatory (1974~1976), which advocated the combination of poetry and jazz.

Both of these two groups had no regulations nor had to pay monthly membership fees. We were free to join them and dismember from them. All we had to do was join the monthly event, called by them as "Poetry at New Jazz," as well as sending the works to the kind of quarterly magazines. Monthly events were held regularly at such places as the New Jazz Hall in Shinjuku, the Kid Ailack Hall in Meidaimae, (it managed by Seiichiro Kuboshima. He was also managing the Shinano Dessin Kan Hall, and the Mugon Kan Hall): The Pulcinella in Shibuya, and The Parco in Ikebukuro. The best highlighted event in my memory was held in the parking lot of the Seibu Department Store in Shibuya, in March, 1972. It had eight hundred audiences. For the event, the poets were Hiroshi Akimura, Sabro Akagi, Fumio Sato, Kazuko Shiraishi, Kosuke Shibusawa, Yu Suwa, Taeko Tomioka, Tetsuo Nakagami, Toyoichiro Miyoshi, Masao Murata, Chuei Yagi, and Gozo Yoshimasu and on the side of the Japan new jazz came on the stage, the Oki Itaru New Jazz Quartet, Masaru Imada, and Yoshiaki Fujikawa of NME Japan. They had the events, just like the Japanese Utagaki, or the festival of tanka or waka poets, with men and women singing and dancing together in the festive mood: the jazz performances of the jazz musicians and the poetry readings of poets could meet and interchange together in their art.

Now I looked back to find that there gathered various characters of poets in The Doin' and The Astronomical Observatory Groups. We, together with the jazz musicians, lasted and continued the reading events for more than ten years. We worked for them, all in the cause of the poetry readings, "Poetry at New Jazz". We were not holding up any kind of the clear manifestation, at the starting point, though, now looking back, I am persuaded that our activity was just an artistic campaign, combined with poetry readings and the New Jazz musicians performed in Tokyo, at that time.

第二部での吉増剛造の「古代天文台」は「すさまじい気迫のぶつかり合いとなり、音が吉増の呪文のような朗読に真正面から挑戦していった」と諏訪優は、その夜のことを記録している。ここに端的に、私たちの詩朗読の、二つの問題が現れている。一つは成果として、一つは反省点として……。

反省点の一つは、ジョー水城に詰問された、学芸会的な詩朗読である。自分の詩集や原稿用紙を手にボソボソ、呟くようなあの朗読である。中上哲夫は「天文台·74年秋号」で次のような問題提起をしている。

「朗読会もずいぶん会を重ねているわけだけど（中略）詩を読む技術論みたいなものがあまり出てこないのは、つねづねおかしなことだと思っている。詩を読む思想論も結構だけれど、技術論もなければ、どうしても片手落ちだ」という提起である。

中上はその前に「発声から始まって、速度、リズム、アクセント、ストレス、イントネーション、エロキューションなどなど、修得しなければならない技術はたくさんある」と述べ、谷川俊太郎の「詩の朗読の技術が、特に日本語の詩の場合には曖昧模糊としている」という言葉を紹介している。

こうした反省が、詩の朗読の技術論として、それ以後渇望されていたのである。もう一つの成果とは、つねにミュージシャンとは対等に、渡り合うということだろう。詩もジャズも初めは模索し合い、ぶつかり合い、やがては調和を見いだすのである。（これは一つの図式にすぎないが）ジャズはここでは詩の伴奏などではない。詩も主張するように、ジャズもまたここでは主張するのである。ということを私たちは、体得したのである。

白石かずこは、近年、白い布地か奉書紙に、墨書きで詩を大きく書き写したものを、朗読している。かつて諏訪優は、「Doin'」創刊号（1962年1月）に、「詩人個々の体臭に満ちたオーラル・メッセージとしての詩を書き、書斎と活字の森から詩を外に出して見るべきだ」と述べ、常づね詩の朗読とは「空間に言葉で詩を書くことだ」と語っていたが、けだし名言であろう。

Now I like to think again on the achievements and the checking points to be improved. It was in December, in 1972, in the Live House OZ in Kichijoji, where we had a poetry reading with the Oki Itaru New Jazz Quartet. It had one hundred eighty audiences. Fifty people could not enter the House and were asked to return. The reading event was proceeding on with excitement and full of tension, when suddenly Joe Mizuki, a drummer, stood up and grasping a mike shouted;

"It is not a school festival! Know it poets! Let's bump into each other! Shall we?"

Immediately we all turned tensed. In the second part, the performance of Gozo Yoshimasu, in "the Ancient Astronomical Observatory" proved into "a kind of bumping together each with the hardest driving spirit, as if the jazz sounds challenging right to his readings like magic spells," noted Yu Suwa. In it, clearly the two points were posed: One for the achievement and, another for the points to be improved.

One of the checks was as Joe Mizuki accused: as in a school performance festival, the poet just murmuring his poem to himself, with the poetry book or the manuscripts in his hands. On the point Tetsuo Nakagami posed a question in the ASTONOMICAL OBSERBATORY in the Autumn Issue, 1974, as following:

"Our reading event we have had so many, but I think it strange that we have not argued on the technique. How should be the poetry reading? It will be, all right, but without any debates on the reading technique, not it will be complete. We need the technical debates."..

He noted that "starting from vocal exercises, speeding, rhythms, accents, stresses and the elocution and so on, we have so many techniques to be mastered." And he quoted the warning by Shuntaro Tanigawa that "the techniques in the poetry reading, especially in the case of the Japanese poetry have not been clearly debated out yet, just in the clouds."

In such reflections, a kind of the theory setting up on the reading technique had come to be required and searched since then. Another fruit was a lesson that poets should always face to interchange with musicians, equally. The poets and musicians, at first, try to grope each other, and then start bumping into each other to find a harmony in the course. Though I may just present you my own chart here, it is clear that the jazz music is not only the

accompaniment to the poems. As the poem insists upon itself, so does the jazz: which we actually learned.,

Kazuko Shiraishi has started reading poems ink-blushed in large letters, on a piece of white cloth or on the Japanese paper, to be rolled. Once Yu Suwa wrote down in the Doin' magazine, in the first issue (published in January, 1962) that we should make poems as oral messages, filled with each unique personality unique, to others. And he used to point out that the poetry reading is just like "writing poems in the air, with words." Surely he said well and just.

(Translator: Noriko Mizusaki. Finished on 2nd of August, 2019)

<会員近況報告・メール情報他> *PANDORA NEWS*

パンドラ・ニュース１

PANDORA NEWS (1)

パンドラ詩の朗読会2019

名称：ポエトリ・リーディングin Tokyo（通称：「パンドラ詩の朗読会」）
内容・目的：参加者による詩の朗読とスピーチ・講話・質疑応答・親睦・国際交流。
参加者は日本国籍に限らない。他言語朗読可（日本語版・英語版が付く場合もあります）。

日　時：2019年8月17日、午後1時より午後5時まで
場　所：日本出版クラブ407号室（東京都千代田区神田神保町1-32）
参加費：スコットさま資料代と会場費カンパ1,000円お願い申し上げます。
本販売：会員の自著をお持ちになり展示ください。販売可。

プログラム
＊13：00pm ～ 14：15pm：参加者による詩朗読とスピーチ・質疑応答。各自10分基本。
＊14：15pm ～ 14：30：休憩
＊14：30pm ～ 15：00： エドワード・レビンソン氏による俳文・自作詩朗読英語。
＊15：00pm ～ 16：00pm：スコット・ワトスン氏によるリーディングと講演。
⑴ < A Special Feature on Santoka >：山頭火特集
種田山頭火の詩集*THE HOME FRONT*：『銃後』・*20Santoka*の解説と俳句の英語訳発表。
山頭火の本制作の説明：ホチキス綴じ、和紙使用、日本画イラスト、少数部作製。
参加者に当本作品を１冊展示、回覧。（購入可）
⑵俳画と山頭火：Mountaintopfire1, 2の展示と朗読。（ku by Santoka, haiga by Shodo, translation by Scott Watson）

＊16：00pm ～ 16：30pm：藤田晴央氏（青森県弘前住）による詩朗読。「さざ波」「春の落日」（日・英で朗読）、「蛇紋岩」（日本語・ドイツ語で朗読）。

＊16：30pm ～ 17：00pm：簡易茶会。（水崎野里子：盆立て）。他詩人も詩朗読・スピーチ可能。

懇親会：終了後。

＊17：30pm ～ 19：30pm：居酒屋なごみ（神田神保町１丁目）会費3,000円。席上スピーチ・詩朗読可。

「パンドラ / PANDORA」刊行委員会代表
水崎野里子記

2019年（令和元年）8月28日 水曜日

寄稿

日本語の詩 翻訳し朗読　藤田 晴央

音感に不思議な味わい

先日、東京・神保町の日本出版クラブにおいて「ポエトリー・リーディングin Tokyo」という催しがあった。これは、日本語の詩と英語に翻訳した詩を併記して、国内外に発信している「パンドラ」という詩誌が開催したものである。私も朗読者の一人として招かれて出席したので、その概要を報告したい。

前半は、詩人と俳人による朗読でスタート。日本詩人クラブ新人賞を受賞している渡辺めぐみさんや渡辺那智子さんが日本語詩を朗読、原詩夏至さん、大原千佳子さん、杏平太さんらが自作を英訳もまじえて朗読。杏さんは自作についてドイツ語でも紹介。エドワード・レビンソンさんは、自作俳句を英語と日本語で朗読した。

後半、東北学院大学のスコット・ワトスン教授による「種田山頭火の俳句」をテーマにした講演が行われた。ワトスン教授は、山頭火（1882～1940年）の俳句を日本語と自らの英語訳で紹介。山頭火の俳句と戦争との関連を考察、仏教とのつながりについても語った。

一例だが、山頭火の「街はおまつりお骨となって帰られたか」の訳は "A town in festival／their sons now bones／come back home"。原句にはない「彼らの息子たち」という単語が入っている。

講演の後、私が「さざ波」「春の落日」の2編を日本語と英語で朗読した。英訳はこの催しの主催者で英文学者の水崎野里子さんである。また、「蛇紋岩」をドイツ語でも朗読。これは主催者の要請を受けて私が下訳したものをケルン大学のモニカ・ウンケル教授に手直しをしてもらったもの。ドイツ語の訳詩について、会場からは「ドイツ語の音の響きが心地良い」という声が上がった。一方、「日本語の原詩がとても詩的なのに翻訳の方は科学的説明が勝ちすぎているのではないか」という意見も出された。

「蛇紋岩」は、早池峰山に登った時、青緑色の岩が登山道や渓流の下に続くのを見て、想を得た詩。恋愛と人生の生き方をからめたものだが、詩の末尾は「青緑の蛇紋岩は／水をしたたらせた蛇のように／うつくしいひとすじの道となり／山頂へとつづいている／ここからは／ひとすじの道」である。「ひとすじの道」は "der gerade Weg"（デア ゲラーデ ヴェーク）。音感が全く違い、不思議な味わいがある。

このようにほかの方々の英語訳も含めて、外国語の音感から新鮮な刺激を得た。日本語を異国の言語に置き直してみることによって、異国人として閉鎖的になっているかもしれない感覚が開かれていくところがあった。自国第一主義が台頭する昨今、心を世界に向かって開いていくことが大切なのではないだろうか。

「パンドラ」では、電子本も刊行しており、海外への発信にも力を入れていくという。規模的にはささやかな催しではあったが、日本において詩を磨いていくということを考える上で、未来志向の良質な企画であったと思う。

（詩人、青森県詩人連盟会長、弘前市）

「ポエトリー・リーディング in Tokyo」で詩を朗読する筆者（中央）

藤田晴央氏報告
（2019年8月28日付　東欧日報）

パンドラ・ニュース 2

PANDORA NEWS (2)

2019年5月～12月：水崎野里子国際アート交流記録

5 月 15 日～ 20 日現地参加：日本モンゴル友好改元記念アートラベル芸術祭（艶麗メダル受賞）

6 月 14 日～ 17 日現地参加：日本シンガポール友好展・初日テープカットと現地の方々を交えた懇親会に参加、会話。

9 月 14 日～ 16 日：世界俳句大会・於東京学士会館・日英でアンソロジー入俳句朗読。

10 月 17 日～ 20 日：日本ヨーロッパ三ケ国（ドイツ・オーストリア）合同交流展・於東京芸術劇場（出品ソネット「花の影」）。

11 月 7 日～ 10 日現地参加：アメリカ翻訳者会議・於ニューヨーク州ロチェスター、ハイアット・レジェンシー・ロチェスターホテル会場。

11 月 8 日～ 12 日：日加友好 90 周年記念日本ケベック友好展加交流展（和歌「たまゆら」日本語・フランス語訳出品参加）

Cette vie,
En un instant
Partie en fumée.
Les éclats pétillants
De la torche s'éteignent.

たまゆらの　もえてはきゆる　このいのち
かがりびあかく　はじけはてたし

Noriko Mizusaki
水崎野里子

Noriko Mizusaki

Shadows of Flowers

I want to step on the shadow of flowers / in the past
like stepping on your shadow
quietly, so as not to be noticed

Step gently, softly
I'm just like a shadow
doing no harm to life

Dew drops
morning / Like crystals
little droplets
shine and roll

I won't cry anymore
because I knew the kindness of flowers
because I knew the gentleness of shadows
tomorrow morning / the dew of light fills the world

会員間のメール交換１

中村朋子さんと水崎野里子

水崎野里子さま：
広島の中村朋子です。
私が所属しています、広島文学資料保存の会が本を出版しました。
一昨日、寄贈の本を１冊、お送りさせていただきました。
よろしくお願いいたします。
中村朋子

中村朋子先生：
お知らせバックありがとうございました。だいぶ読み応えのあるご本ですね。
私は演劇の方にも首を突っ込んでおりますので嬉しく存じます。土屋さまのご活躍に感謝です。ヒロシマの文化人は強いですね。御恵送ありがとうございます。
水崎野里子拝

水崎野里子さま：
帰国早々でお疲れのところ、早速にお返事をいただきありがとうございます。
この本の出版に関しては、会長の土屋時子さんが中心になり取り組みました。
私は、完成した本の広報のお手伝いをと思いまして、お送りさせていただきました。
水崎さまの益々のご活躍をお祈りしております。
中村朋子
Date: Sun, 25 Aug 2019 18:06:

解説

中村朋子先生と水崎のメール間で言及されている著作本とは、土屋時子・八木良広編『ヒロシマの河　劇作家・土屋清の青春群像劇』(2019年８月６日、藤原書店刊) である。

著作は、広島生まれの劇作家土屋清 (1930-87) による、生前の峠三吉を主人公として登場させた創作劇『河』(1963年に広島で初演)台本を最後に再録させ、それに至るまでかなりの頁数を活用して、むしろ土屋清の生涯と、彼の創作劇『河』上演前後の経緯について、土屋清自身と出版責任の土屋時子さんの論考をふくめた総勢14名の論考から成る356頁に亘る労作である。土屋時子さんは1948年(戦後)生まれ、1971年4月から2009年3月まで広島女学院大学に図書館司書として勤務しながら劇団活動を続けた。土屋時子さんの『河』の上演参加は1983年、1988年と明記されている。いわば当時、平和運動家・女優として土屋清と『河』上演に参加した若かった女史が、56年の長い歳月を経て再び土屋清と『河』上演に回帰した。その経緯と持続と努力は本書に一貫して流れる河、反核への熱意と読者に迫る。

著作の特色は、まず、土屋清による『河』の初演の年・1963年前後の広島における反核運動の状況を、当時の米ソ・中国・日本を含む世界的な反核運動の葛藤の中で読者に提示させたことにあろう。1955年第一回原水爆禁止世界大会は開催されるが、国外と国内の多様な反核状況の反映を受けて1963年の第九回世界大会は「原水協」(原水爆禁止日本協議会)と「原水禁」(原水爆禁止日本国民会議)へと分裂する。その混乱の中で『河』は、前夜祭として平和公園内の広島市公会堂で職場演劇合同公演として初演された。以降、本劇は日本国中で上演されて行くが、綿密に記録された上演記録には御礼申し上げたい。

本著の特色はゆえに、劇の主人公峠三吉(1917-1953)の考証よりもむしろほとんど無名で終わった土屋清という一人の平和運動家・劇作家と彼の創作劇を忘却の歴史の闇から引きずり出し、ライトをあてたことにあろう。いわば彼を舞台に立たせ再生させ、彼と劇『河』の歴史性と歴史的な背景を詳細と言って良いほどに追及し、複数の書き手によって各視点からそれぞれ記載させた。土屋時子さんは、広島の反核運動をいわば「河」として、まず1945年8月6日の広島への原爆投下、1950年の朝鮮戦争の勃発、1953年の峠三吉の死を経て1963年の当劇の初演・原水協と原水禁への分裂に至るまでの広島の、苦難を極めた反核運動の状況を流れとして記載した。次いでその苦難を極めた・極める歴史の河を、現在、2019年時点での東アジア・朝鮮半島をめぐる同じく世界的な国々の確執の中での、相も変わらず自国の利益と困難と挫折・不成功を繰り返す国際的な反核状況に結び付けた。女史をはじめとする広島中心の日本の反核運動に見る、たゆまぬ努力と持続に賛意と賞賛を捧げたい。改めて驚嘆と敬意を感じたことを付け加えたい。沈黙は放棄だ。それを改めて感じさせてくれた大著である。

若かったひとりの女優として『河』上演に参加し、土屋清というほとんど他県では無名で終わった劇作家の生きざまに立ち会い、約60年間、その二つの存在への愛と熱意を保ち続け、老いた今となって改めて光をあて、これだけの評者と内容を集められる状況まで成長し得たひとりの女の生涯の記録と証としても読める。土屋清から受け継いだ平和への熱意は美しい。総指揮・総編集は見事である。ヒロシマの河はまだ死んではいない。

（2019年9月 21日脱稿）

会員間のメール交換２

ウベ・ワルターさんと水崎野里子

uwe walter さん:
Thanks for your sending us your precious essay. I am sending forward to the editor, Kuroda san.
I was astonished at your fluent Japanese. I learned German a little, but in vain. Noriko

ウベ・ワルターさん：
貴重なエッセイ送って下さりありがとうございました。
編集の黒田さんに転送します。貴兄の流暢な日本語に驚きました。
私はドイツ語を少し学びましたが忘れました。のりこ拝

Noriko さん
以前書いたエッセイを送りします。

＜Handicap?　心のバリアーフリー 本質を見る＞

人を見かけで 判断するのは楽しいであり、その人が社会的規範の枠から外れていなければきちんとしていると感じ安心するものである。

左ハンドルの車に乗る人には“すごいなあ”と思ってしまい、ルイ・ビトンのハンドバッグを持っている人に対しては“良いもの持ってる、なあ”などと感じてしまう。それはまるで尊敬に近いくらいである。

日本の伝陶芸に携われる人は着物を身につつみ、ロックミュジシャンは長い噛髪の毛をしている——
これはあたりまえのようだが、もしかれらがこのような外観でないとしたら……？　知的であるが故、または別の理由でこうした捨ステイタスシンボル・スタイルにこだわらない人と言うのもいるのである。

つまりその人の真の姿戸外見は、いわゆる常識で一致しないケースであり、それはたとえばこの社会での弱者である。物資のあふれる中での所有戦争に敗北した脱出者、消費主義を拒絶する人、そしてなるべ

く人目にさらさずにおこうとされてしまう障害者、そう言った人たちである。障害者の為にわ様々な施設、収容機関あるいは最近では作業所などがあり、その中でならば、彼等国民総生産増大に貢献することが許されるのである。しかし彼等を人目につかない所へ押しやると言う、そんな隔離対策が本当に必要であろうか？

ここに私の頭にしつこいくらいに浮かんで来るのが、美人と車椅子の人との比較である。どちらも、それぞれの外見で判断されてしまい、それぞれの真の姿と言うのは認識される事がないと言う点では共通している。その人の本質にたどり着く、本当の姿を見つける、と言う事はとても難しく、その為には自分の心を真っ白の状態にしておかなくてはならない。

人間は自己と他人を比べたがるものでその上自分を他人よりも上に置ずげたがったり、あるいは優位たった気持ちで、同情を寄せてみたりする。

美人がいるとその外見を楽しみ、何か特別な“いいもモノ”みなすが車椅子の人に対しては上から下に向かって口を聞き、その際自分が健康であることをひそかに嬉しく思ってしまったりする。

ただ美人にしても車椅子の人にしても、結局はその姿形ゆえに、うわべだけの認識がされがちであり、本質にまで目お向けてもらえず、気の毒だと言えよう。

目に見える障害者だけでなく、実は“フツーの人々”のなかにいる一見“フツーに見える障害者”をご存じだろうか？

誤った判断力を持った人は“きちんとした職業”に就いていることが有る。例えば“大人”になっていないまま、良い大学に送り込まれ、やがてサラリーマンになった＜判断力障害者＞などである。

自分の夢に目を向けない、金勘定や日々のスケジュールで思い込んで、他人との付き合いからは得になることだけを捜している、真の幸福と言うものを知らない、自分の出した結論の中でさえも本当の意味での自由を持っていない、想像力や創造情をなくしている……そんな人々は自分が作ったバリアの中に暮らしている。

だからバリアフリー出て来て話し合いの場（ランド）造りましょう！

一つの出逢いの場 創造情と生きる喜び

ここでは身体・精神障害者だって優遇されることなく能力に応じて畑仕事、冒険広場、家屋建築・企画／会議に参加してもらいます。

見て見ぬふり＝文化の違い

ある日、お婆さんが坂道をおりて来た。

私秩序正しく、徹底的、丁寧に土壁を塗るしぐさをじっとみつめて

“ドイツにも土壁あるのかい”？

私が振り向いた。

“はい、私のおばさんは900年前に建てた土壁の家に住んでいます。”

“まだゲルマンの神様の字が壁に書いてあります。”

そのとたんに壁が落た。

おばあさんが浴びた壁土をはらってから家に帰った。

“がらがら”とドアを開け、がらがらとドアを閉めると反対側の壁が崩れた。

沈黙。

隣の家の家族がどっと爆笑。日本人は家に帰ってから笑う。

やっぱり文化は違う。

よろしく御願いします

u.w.

＜エッセイ２＞

50億年前に小惑星が地球に衝突しました。その結果、地球の地軸chijikuが23.5度傾ました。

この事件のおかげで、地球に生命にとって可能な環境が作られました。太陽からの光で水が蒸発して、それでできた雲が天気を作り出します。

地球をまとうているごく薄い大気が我々を空気で養う。その上に厳しい寒さの宇宙が限りなく広がっている。この天体は、表面は接する宇宙に冷されて固まっていますが、いまだに内部では灼熱のマグマが煮えたぎり、時折　火山を通して地表 に噴出されます。

地球は呼吸している有機体であると思います。地球のすべての生命は繋がっています。すべては互いを補いながら存在しています。人間はこの素晴らしいバランスを破壊する権利を持っていないと思う。

地球上の資源を、取り尽くす、捕り尽くす、狩り尽くす、刈り尽くす、掘り尽くす、汲み上げ尽くす、伐り尽くす　という考え方は「強欲」の心の病気です。その病気に置かされている権力者に権力の権利を取り上げるべきと思います。

Am Di., 19. Nov. 2019 um 12:18 Uhr schrieb uwe walter <ubewaruta57@gmail.com>:

＜エッセイ３＞

日本海が鮮やかに水平線のかなたまで広がりました。雪に覆われた山形の高い山々、が夕日に赤みを帯びました。

夜被災地に近づいたのは匂いで分かりました。

へドロに覆われた瓦礫畑。途中でパチンコの遺跡、無制限に24時間買物出来る便利屋ローソン：
経済着成長のシンボル、現代の消費宮殿が今、ドアや窓は、ボードで釘付け。

虚無僧の心、古典本曲で冥福を祈るために津波が残しておいた瓦礫の中歩きまわりました、音を永遠にのばしてが、最後まで吐く、突然、一撃で音を切る、生と死、予測しがたい。

泥染みが付いた結婚のアルバム、母親と一緒に写った着物姿の花嫁 を見つけ、私は吹かずにはいられなかった。「ごめん、ね。遅く成りました。わずかな贈り物としてセレナーデを演奏します。」と対話をしました。

生命を敬う死者への敬意「安産」という古典本曲を吹きました。

Am Di., 19. Nov. 2019 um 12:18 Uhr schrieb uwe walter <ubewaruta57@gmail.com>:

PS：２年前の京都新聞の取材です。

監視社会の細音
② 父の死
自由求めるデモで撃たれ

監視社会の細音
⑩ 盗聴器
密告者がどこかにいる

監視社会の細音
⑦ 共謀罪
民主主義守るなら努力を

（日本語：ウベ・ワルター）

会員消息

エドワード・レビンソンさんの写真展
「オリンパスギャラリー東京」（西新宿）にて
2019 年 11 月 15 日㈮～ 20 日㈬
原詩夏至氏、奥様来訪。

The Message Card for a Photo Exhibition Crafted by Edward Levinson.
At the Tokyo・Orinpus Gallery.
15th -20th, November, 2019.
Mr. &Mrs. Hara Visited.

あとがき

本年も皆様に『パンドラV』をお送りします。海外詩人と日本詩人協力のアート誌、日本語と他言語（英語メイン）使用の、日本では数少ないマルチリンガル誌として果たすべき役割は大きく、本年も境を越えた世界の友好と平和を世界へ向けて発信します。会員・投稿の皆さまの結束と協力とご寛容は本年も大きく、感謝・御礼申し上げます。

昨年2019年9月から10月にかけての日本の颱風被害は多大で、私の居住する千葉県もかなりの被害を受けました。全国からのお励ましのお電話と支援に御礼申し上げると共に、被災地域の方々には災害お見舞い申し上げます。なお、今後の被害対策・政策の完備（停電・河氾濫・ひとり暮らしの老人の孤独死など）へのさらなるアプローチ、取り組みを皆さまにもよろしくお願い申し上げます。

末筆になりますが本号もブックウエイ出版社と編集の黒田貴子様にお世話いただきました。
こころより御礼申し上げます。

2020年春吉日
パンドラ刊行委員会
水崎野里子

「パンドラＶ」

刊 行 日：2020年5月24日
版権取得：2020年5月24日
発 行 所：273－0031千葉県船橋市西船2－20－7－204水崎方
「パンドラ」刊行委員会
Ｅメールアドレス：the-mizusaki@pop21.odn.ne.jp
ファクス・電話：047-434-8579
印刷所・発売元：Book Way 書店（姫路）
TEL：079-222-5372　FAX：079-244-1482
Ｅメール：info@bookway.jp
https://bookway.jp/shuppan/

ISBN978-4-86584-456-6
「パンドラＶ」はE-Bookとしても購入可能です。
紙製本・電子本：1,700円（＋税）US$17.00

The First Edition: May 2020.
Copyright: May 2020
The Members' Office of the PANDORA Books:
c/o Noriko Mizusaki,
2-20-7-204, Nishifuna, Funabashi-shi, Chiba, 273-0031, Japan
TEL/FAX: 047-434-8579, International: 81-47-434-8579
The Publication & Sales Store: Bookway (in Himeji, Japan)
TEL 079-222-5372 FAX: 079-244-1482
E-mail: info@bookway.jp
https://bookway.jp/shuppan/
ISBN978-4-86584-456-6

You can also read "PANDORA V" in the E-Book.
A Paper Book & E-Book: ￥1,700 (+tax)　US$17.00
刊行日時：2020年5月24日